The Pocket Encyclopaedia of World Aircraft in Colour

HELICOPTERS

AND OTHER ROTORCRAFT SINCE 1907

The Pocket Encyclopaedia
of World Aircraft in Colour

HELICOPTERS

AND OTHER ROTORCRAFT SINCE 1907

by

KENNETH MUNSON

Illustrated by
JOHN W. WOOD
Frank Friend
Brian Hiley
William Hobson
Alan Holliday
Tony Mitchell
Allen Randall

LONDON
BLANDFORD PRESS

First published in 1968
Revised edition copyright © 1973 Blandford Press Ltd.
Reprinted 1975
167 High Holborn, London, WC1V 6PH

ISBN 7137 06104

Colour printed by The Ysel Press, Deventer, Holland
Text printed and books bound in England
by Richard Clay (The Chaucer Press), Ltd,
Bungay, Suffolk

PREFACE

Among the many rewarding aspects of a series such as this is the opportunity which it provides for including categories of aircraft that are less freely covered than others by current works of reference. The volumes on *Private, Business and General Purpose Aircraft* and *Pioneer Aircraft 1903–14* have more than justified their existence, and *Helicopters* covers another class in which contemporary references are comparatively scarce. Moreover, this volume is to the best of my belief unique in the joint respects of presenting a comprehensive range of historic and modern rotorcraft in this form, and of doing so in colour.

In this revised edition, by virtue of a little judicious rearrangement, the number of rotorcraft illustrated has been increased from 82 to 94, yet only four types which were present in the original edition have been omitted from the present volume.

As always, this is a team effort, not only between myself, our indefatigable colour researcher Ian Huntley and the artists responsible, under John Wood, for the individual plates, but aided by the generous co-operation given by manufacturers, operators and others. In this last category I am delighted to acknowledge specific assistance by Jean Alexander, R. G. Austin, Mário Roberto vaz Carneiro, Lt-Col N. Kindberg of the Royal Swedish Air Force, Jørgen Lundø of Politikens Forlag, Copenhagen, Philip J. R. Moyes, Stephen Peltz, John W. R. Taylor, Wg Cdr K. H. Wallis (RAF Retd) and John W. Wickenden, without whom the selection of contents would have been less complete and certainly less colourful; by Basil Arkell, John Fay and H. D. Leigh for technical advice; and by Pamela Matthews, whose help and advice while typing the manuscript and reading the proofs were, as ever, of immense value.

October, 1972

INTRODUCTION

Although contributory aspects of vertical flight principles can trace their origins back to Archimedes, or even earlier to the ancient Chinese, credit for the modern invention of the helicopter belongs to the 15th-century Italian artist, architect, engineer and philosopher Leonardo da Vinci. Around A.D. 1500, da Vinci sketched out a design for what he called a 'helical screw', powered by a spring mechanism – thereby taking, incidentally, at least part of the credit for inventing the word helicopter, which is derived from the Greek *helix* (spiral) and *pteron* (wing). It has not been established whether flight was actually achieved by da Vinci's device, and by the time his sketch was generally published in 1881 other model helicopters had already been flown successfully. The first of these was the little toy designed and made by the French naturalist Launoy and his colleague Bienvenu, a mechanic, in 1784. Demonstrated before the Académie des Sciences, it was a simple device consisting of a short pole, on to which a bow was threaded with the bowstring twisted round the length of the pole. When released, the unwinding string provided enough force to rotate two pairs of blades at each end of the pole. This little toy thus became the first heavier-than-air powered machine known to have made a successful journey through the air, but it was to be another one hundred and twenty-three years before the first noteworthy man-carrying helicopters made their appearance.

Appropriately, perhaps, these were also French in origin, but the designs both of the Breguet brothers and of Paul Cornu can be regarded as only the first hesitant steps along the path towards a truly practical helicopter, a point not reached for another thirty years. During that time various pioneers of rotating-wing flight produced designs that contributed in one way or another towards the achievement of practical helicopter flight, and a small selection of these aircraft appears in this volume. But by far the greatest contribution was that made by the Spaniard, Juan de la Cierva, when he accomplished the successful evolution of his Autogiro between 1923 and 1936. The very success of the Autogiro, a first cousin of the 'pure' helicopter, may have drawn the attention of some designers away from the study of

7

helicopters, but at the same time it brought about a far wider understanding of the problems of rotary-winged flight that was of immeasurable value to the ultimate evolution of the successful helicopter.

An autogyro, like an orthodox aeroplane, achieves its forward thrust by means of a conventionally mounted engine and propeller; but, whereas the aeroplane derives lift from a fixed wing, the autogyro does so by means of a freely rotating wing, or rotor, which, as Cierva eventually discovered, produces a significant amount of lift even at low forward speeds. The helicopter combines aspects of both by using its engine to *drive* the rotor, thus providing lift enabling the machine to hover or climb vertically and, with the disc of the rotor tilted in the required direction of flight, propulsion enabling the machine to translate to horizontal flight. Because of this dual function, the helicopter has a distinct advantage over the autogyro, which, although it requires only small forward speeds to maintain its lift and can take off and land in extremely short distances, is still not a direct-lift machine capable of true hovering flight. In the event of an engine failure, the helicopter's rotor can be put into autorotation by decreasing the blade pitch, thus transforming it into an autogyro and enabling it to descend safely without power, the rotor acting as a 'windmilling' brake.

To derive the necessary lift for vertical take-off, the rotor of a helicopter must clearly be of much greater diameter than the propeller of a conventional aeroplane, and consequently must also rotate much more slowly. The gearing of the engine to drive the rotor results in a turning moment (torque) of the rotor shaft that creates a tendency by the fuselage to turn in the opposite direction. This effect is counteracted (in helicopters with a single main rotor) by using an engine-driven tail rotor of smaller dimensions, revolving in a vertical plane; with variation of thrust this also provides directional control. In helicopters employing co-axial, intermeshing or tandem main rotors, the rotors rotate in opposite directions, hence the torque from each cancels out that of the other. In the co-axial configuration, directional control is achieved by means of differential power supplied to the rotors, creating a change in torque which turns the fuselage. In the intermeshing or tandem configurations it is achieved by tilting the rotor discs in opposite directions to one another.

8

Vertical control of a single main rotor helicopter, which involves altering the thrust of the main rotor, is carried out by a collective pitch change – altering the pitch angles of all the main rotor blades simultaneously, in the same direction and by the same amount. During this change the rotor r.p.m. must be maintained at approximately the same figure. Forward, sideways or backward flight is carried out by tilting the rotor's plane of rotation in the required direction by means of cyclic pitch changes. A cyclic pitch change causes the pitch of each blade to alter continuously as it revolves, so that while any given blade is increasing pitch the blade diametrically opposite is decreasing pitch, and vice versa. Changes of lift caused by changes of pitch tend to make the blades rise or fall on their horizontal (or 'flapping') hinges so that, in effect, the whole rotor disc is tilted. Thus, for forward movement, the pitch of the retreating blade is increased, causing it to flap upward to reach its highest position at the rear of the fuselage; at the same time the advancing blade's pitch is decreased so that it is at its lowest position at the front of the aircraft. With the rotor disc thus tilted, the vertical thrust component provides lift while the horizontal component, introduced by the tilting, provides propulsion.

During rotation of the rotor, cyclic bending loads can be created at the blade roots and, to prevent these, vertical hinges called 'drag hinges' (or 'lag hinges') may be fitted to the blades, permitting them to move to and fro horizontally in relation to the hub or to each other. Drag hinges in turn must be fitted with friction or hydraulic 'drag dampers', between each rotor blade and the hub, which damp down unstable dragging motions of the blades as they revolve and thus tend to maintain them in correct relationship to one another. Without these drag dampers, the drag hinges could permit the blades to be displaced cyclically in such a manner that the rotor's centre of gravity could become offset from its geometric centre. Continued rotation of such an unbalanced system would result in a strong oscillation of the fuselage, producing – if the aircraft is on the ground – the phenomenon known as ground resonance. This would result if the oscillation were in phase with the natural frequency of the fuselage about the undercarriage or tyres, when the oscillation would increase in amplitude, causing the aircraft to bounce from side to side until finally it broke up or rolled over.

9

The gradual establishment of the pure helicopter as a practical form of vehicle began in the early 1930s. Pescara's early efforts included a primitive form of collective control, although the machines were not very stable, and the 1935 Gyroplane Laboratoire built by Louis Breguet and René Dorand included both collective and cyclic pitch controls. A year after the French machine had flown the little German Fw 61 began to eclipse it in performance with a series of world height, speed and distance records that were remarkable for their time; but not until Sikorsky, after more than two years' flight development, brought his VS-300 to its ultimate state at the close of 1941, could the helicopter be said to have become a practical vehicle capable of carrying a useful load as well as a pilot and thereby able to do a real job of work. In the thirty years that have followed the VS-300, the tasks performed by helicopters of all shapes and sizes have, as one commentator expressed it, 'multiplied like rabbits'. A much-quoted letter written by Wilbur Wright in January 1906 reveals that this knowledgeable and respected pioneer of aviation did not think much of the helicopter as a means of flight – mostly for the wrong reasons, but one incontrovertible remark he made in this letter was that 'the helicopter does with great labor only what the balloon does without labor'. He might, even more appropriately, have said that it did only what the fixed-wing aeroplane did with far less labour, for undoubtedly the biggest barrier to the helicopter's progress has been that, pound for pound of payload, the helicopter required a powerplant of much greater output than a conventional aeroplane. This inevitably meant that its running costs were considerably higher, and consequently its main sponsors in the formative years of its operating life were government and military organisations rather than commercial undertakings. The limitations of power and operating costs, and the ancillary problems of reliability and control stability to be expected in a relatively untried form of vehicle, meant that for many years helicopters were confined in the main to rescue work and various specialised tasks beyond the capability of other kinds of craft. Even now this type of work still constitutes the principal activity of the helicopter, though it has widened immeasurably in scope, especially in the realms of agriculture and industry. The helicopter has the enviable record of having done more in practical and humanitarian terms than any other individual type of vehicle to save lives, to relieve suffering and hardship and to improve standards of living in many parts of the world; but it has taken a long time for the image of expensive toy or stunt vehicle to be replaced by that of the serious and practical aircraft.

One of the major obstacles has been the attitude of the public at large to the noise made by helicopters, especially in built-up areas. The truth of this matter, which is too obvious for many people to see, is that the helicopter is still very much of a novelty in all but a few city centres. Automatically, therefore, when it does appear it is a focal point of attention and people are accordingly more aware of the noise it makes; but to argue from this that it actually makes more noise than it does is false reasoning. Scientific tests of sound levels and frequencies carried out under a variety of conditions have demonstrated repeatedly that helicopter noise is usually no greater than (say) that of underground trains, heavy lorries, industrial machinery or other familiar ingredients of modern city life; nor does it usually continue for so long.

The first big breakthrough in making the helicopter a viable proposition from a commercial standpoint came in the latter half of the 1950s, when it became possible to introduce gas turbines as a source of power instead of the heavy, expensive-to-operate piston-engines previously used. Not only are turbines smaller in size, offering a far superior power-to-weight ratio, but they are more efficient and easier to maintain than a piston-engine. Increases in aerodynamic efficiency (and thus in payload capability) have resulted from more recent improvements in rotor blade design; allied to these the gas turbine, despite its high initial cost, now offers the civilian operator a much more viable commercial proposition. Before the general introduction of turbine-powered machines a number of helicopter airlines – notably Chicago Helicopter Airways, Los Angeles Airways and New York Airways in the United States, and British European Airways and Sabena in Europe – operated scheduled passenger-carrying services with piston-engined types. But these were more in the nature of a gesture of faith than a commercial proposition, and were heavily backed by government subsidies. The need for such subsidies was first broken in 1960, when San Francisco & Oakland Helicopters Inc introduced the single-turbine Sikorsky

S-62A into service; and two years later, with the appearance of the twin-engined Boeing-Vertol 107 and the Sikorsky S-61L, commercial helicopters were at last available that could carry a substantial number of passengers and whose operating economics, in the words of one observer, 'no longer looked like something out of *Alice in Wonderland*'.

We are, of course, still paying the price, in terms of higher costs, lower payloads and slower speeds, that is inevitable in any comparison between helicopters and fixed-wing aircraft. Many consider it a small price to pay to avoid the ever-increasing appetite for concrete of present and future generations of jet airliners. But those who do not agree should at least be encouraged by the knowledge that helicopter performance is today on the threshold of another major step forward.

In the early years of helicopter evolution it was simpler for designers to separate the means of achieving vertical and forward thrust; then, with the development of cyclic pitch control and 'flapping' rotor blades, practical pure helicopters were achieved that used the rotor for both lift and forward thrust, without resorting to the added complication (and weight) of supplementary means of propulsion. However, it has been apparent for some time that the forward flight performance of helicopters designed in accordance with hitherto-conventional technology has virtually reached the limit of which they are capable. Current helicopters have a practical maximum speed which is dictated by a variety of factors including drag, stalling of the retreating blades, and compressibility effects on the tips of the advancing blades as their speed approaches that of sound. The pure helicopter thus reaches a practical limit for forward speed at little more than 200 mph (322 km/hr), and designs such as the Rotodyne and the Russian Ka-22, excellent though they were, could not offer any significant improvement upon this. Some limited improvement of existing designs has been found by adding stub wings to relieve the rotor of part of its lifting duty, and in certain cases by providing a supplementary means of forward propulsion as well; but the limitations of lightly-stressed, hinged rotor systems still remain. The steps now being taken to overcome these limitations concern the development of satisfactory rigid-rotor systems and the evolution of compound helicopters using such systems.

The renewed interest in the rigid (or hingeless) rotor system has been prompted by the fact that such a system has a number of significant advantages, especially at higher speeds, over the conventional system, and is seen as an essential prerequisite to overcoming the helicopter's basic speed limitations. The essential feature of the hingeless rotor system is the removal of the conventional flapping and lagging hinges. Because of the resulting cantilever action of the blades, large hub moments can be developed which form a powerful source of pitching and rolling control moment, and damping moment. The current designs, in contrast to early rigid rotors, do not attempt to avoid flexibility at the hub; instead, they utilise predetermined amounts of flexibility in order to control the rotor suspense, blade stresses and vibration level. This results in a significant and much-needed improvement in the handling qualities of the helicopter, while the removal of the hinges and their associated mechanism reduces substantially the complexity and aerodynamic drag of the rotor hub, and simplifies maintenance and overhaul.

A compound helicopter is simply a pure helicopter which employs a supplementary means of forward thrust instead of tilting the rotor disc forward to achieve the same purpose. The idea is not a new one – indeed, by definition, Ellehammer's little machine of 1912 was a compound helicopter, since its 6-cylinder engine drove a tractor propeller as well as the rotor. In current designs it is usual to add small fixed wings which unload the rotor progressively as the wings generate lift as the forward speed increases. However, even into the 1960s the performance margin of compound helicopters over contemporary 'pure' helicopters was scarcely enough to justify the additional design complexity, not because the airframes or powerplants were inadequate but because there was no satisfactory rotor system capable of operating efficiently at much above 200 mph. The rigid rotor provides an initial answer to this problem, and the increased performance capability which it brings has already been seen in the Lockheed XH-51A which is the fastest compound helicopter yet to fly. In 1965 the XH-51A achieved a level speed of 272 mph (438 km/hr). This record remained unbeaten until exceeded by the same aircraft in June 1967, when it reached 302·6 mph (487 km/hr). These speeds were achieved using a 4-blade rigid rotor, virtually the same as that on the 200 mph pure helicopter version of the XH-51A, and not one designed specifically for high speed flight. Some of the experience gained with the XH-51A research aircraft was incorporated into the military AH-56A Cheyenne, and despite the cancellation of the Cheyenne programme Lockheed is to continue its development work on rigid rotor systems. Elsewhere, Sikorsky is to test its new ABC (Advancing Blade Concept) system in its S-69 research helicopter. This system, consisting of two co-axial contra-rotating rigid rotors, takes advantage of the blades' aerodynamic lift on the advancing side of each rotor disc, achieving full lift capability on the advancing blades without a penalty being imposed by the retreating blades.

It is fair to draw a comparison between the present state of compound helicopter development and that existing in the early 1940s when the pure helicopter was first put into quantity production. Experimentally, too, we are in sight of developing successful convertible helicopters in which the rotors can be used for lift only, afterwards being stopped in flight and the blades folded and retracted into the fuselage, leaving the aircraft free to continue its forward flight in the same manner as a conventional fixed-wing aeroplane.

THE COLOUR PLATES

As an aid to identification, the colour illustrations that follow
have been arranged on a generally visual basis. The 'split' plan
view gives upper and lower surface markings within a single
outline, but for the sake of clarity asymmetric features such as
offset tail rotors or half-tailplanes have been shown in one aspect
only. The reference number of each aircraft corresponds to the
appropriate text matter. A glossary of rotorcraft terms begins on
p. 189, and an index to all types appears on pp. 197–200.

BREGUET-RICHET No.1 (France)

CORNU (France)

ELLEHAMMER (Denmark)

1

Breguet-Richet *Gyroplane* No. 1, September 1907. *Engine:* One 40/45 h.p. Antoinette piston-engine. *Rotor diameter (each):* 26 ft. 3 in. (8·00 m.). *Total area of lifting surfaces:* 279·86 sq. ft. (26·00 sq. m.). *Empty weight:* 1,102 lb. (500 kg.). *Take-off weight:* 1,274 lb. (578 kg.).

2

Paul Cornu helicopter, November 1907. *Engine:* One 24 h.p. Antoinette piston-engine. *Rotor diameter (each):* 19 ft. 8¼ in. (6·00 m.). *Length:* approx. 20 ft. 4⅛ in. (6·20 m.). *Empty weight:* 419 lb. (190 kg.). *Take-off weight:* 573 lb. (260 kg.).

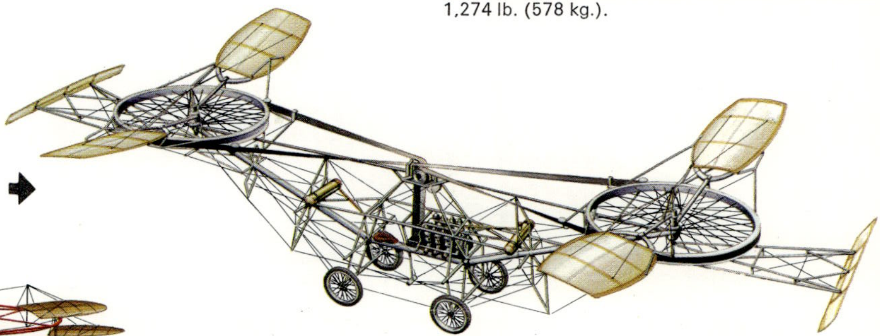

3

Ellehammer helicopter of 1912. *Engine:* One 36 h.p. Ellehammer air-cooled radial piston-engine. *Rotor diameter (each):* 24 ft. 6⅛ in. (7·47 m.). No other details known.

17

OEHMICHEN No. 2 (France)

PESCARA No. 3 (Spain)

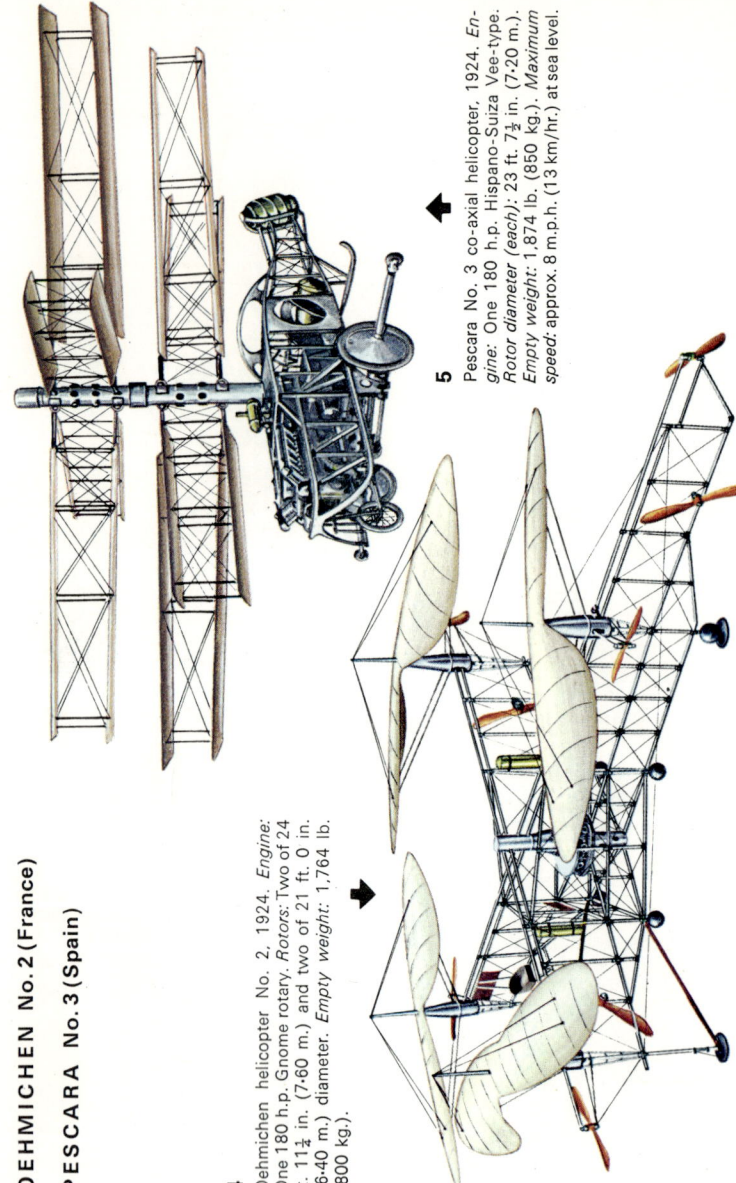

4

Oehmichen helicopter No. 2. 1924. *Engine:* One 180 h.p. Gnome rotary. *Rotors:* Two of 24 ft. 11¼ in. (7·60 m.) and two of 21 ft. 0 in. (6·40 m.) diameter. *Empty weight:* 1,764 lb. (800 kg.).

5

Pescara No. 3 co-axial helicopter. 1924. *Engine:* One 180 h.p. Hispano-Suiza Vee-type. *Rotor diameter (each):* 23 ft. 7½ in. (7·20 m.). *Empty weight:* 1,874 lb. (850 kg.). *Maximum speed:* approx. 8 m.p.h. (13 km/hr.) at sea level.

18

6

Cierva C.8L Mk. II which made the first cross-Channel flight by a rotary-winged aeroplane on 18 September 1928; now exhibited in the *Musée de l'Air*, Paris. *Engine:* One 200 h.p. Armstrong Siddeley Lynx IVc seven-cylinder radial. *Rotor diameter:* 39 ft. 8 in. (12·09 m.). *Fuselage length:* 28 ft. 6 in. (8·69 m.). *Height:* 14 ft. 9 in. (4·50 m.). *Maximum take-off weight:* 2,470 lb. (1,120 kg.). *Maximum speed:* 100 m.p.h. (161 km/hr.) at sea level. *Cruising altitude:* 3,937 ft. (1,200 m.). *Range:* 255 miles (410 km.).

7

Avro Rota (Cierva C.30A) of No. 529 Squadron R.A.F., 1944. *Engine:* One 140 h.p. Armstrong Siddeley Genet Major seven-cylinder radial. *Rotor diameter:* 37 ft. 0 in. (11·28 m.). *Fuselage length:* 19 ft. 8½ in. (6·01 m.). *Height:* 11 ft. 1 in. (3·38 m.). *Maximum take-off weight:* 1,900 lb. (862 kg.). *Maximum speed:* 110 m.p.h. (177 km./hr.) at sea level. *Service ceiling:* 8,000 ft. (2,438 m.). *Range on internal fuel:* 250 miles (402 km.).

8

TsAGI (Kuznetsov) 2-EA Autogiro, *ca.* 1931. *Engine:* One 230 h.p. Gnome-Rhône Titan five-cylinder radial. *Rotor diameter:* 39 ft. 4½ in. (12·00 m.). *Wing span:* 22 ft. 0¾ in. (6·73 m.). *Fuselage length:* 20 ft. 7¾ in. (6·295 m.). *Height (flying attitude):* 12 ft. 10 in. (3·91 m.). *Maximum take-off weight:* 2,275 lb. (1,032 kg.). *Maximum speed:* 99·4 m.p.h. (160 km/hr.). *Ceiling:* 13,780 ft. (4,200 m.). *Endurance:* 1 hr. 45 min.

9

TsAGI (Kuznetsov) A-4 Autogiro, *ca.* 1933. *Engine:* One 300 h.p. M-26 seven-cylinder radial. *Rotor diameter:* 42 ft. 7¾ in. (13·00 m.). *Wing span:* 22 ft. 0¾ in. (6·73 m.). *Fuselage length:* 23 ft. 8¼ in. (7·22 m.). *Height (flying attitude):* 13 ft. 6¼ in. (4·123 m.). *Maximum take-off weight:* 2,866 lb. (1,300 kg.). *Maximum speed:* 109·4 m.p.h. (176 km/hr.). *Ceiling:* 13,450 ft. (4,100 m.).

10

TsAGI (Skrzhinskii) A-12 Autogiro, *ca.* 1936. *Engine:* One 640 h.p. Wright Cyclone F-3 nine-cylinder radial. *Rotor diameter:* 45 ft. 11¼ in. (14·00 m.). *Fuselage length:* 22 ft. 1¼ in. (6·74 m.). *Height (flying attitude):* approx 11 ft. 5¾ in. (3·50 m.). *Maximum take-off weight:* 3,719 lb. (1,687 kg.). *Maximum speed:* 152 m.p.h. (245 km/hr.). *Ceiling:* 18,275 ft. (5,570 m.).

KELLETT KD-1 (U.S.A.)

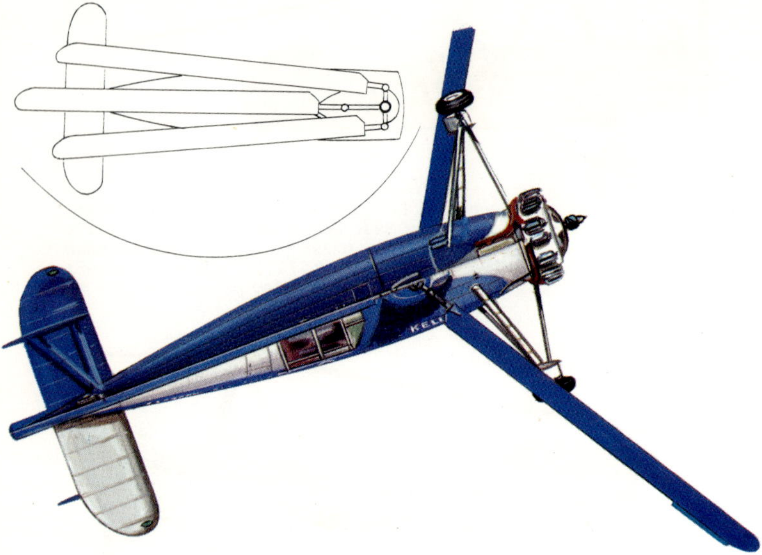

11

Kellett KD-1B of Eastern Air Lines Inc., July 1939. *Engine:* One 225 h.p. Jacobs L-4MA seven-cylinder radial. *Rotor diameter:* 40 ft. 0 in. (12·19 m.). *Length overall (blades folded):* 28 ft. 10 in. (8·79 m.). *Height:* 10 ft. 3 in. (3·12 m.). *Maximum take-off weight:* 2,250 lb. (1,020 kg.). *Maximum speed:* 127 m.p.h. (204 km./hr.) at sea level. *Service ceiling:* 14,000 ft. (4,267 m.). *Typical range:* 200 miles (322 km.).

GYROPLANE LABORATOIRE (France)

12

Breguet-Dorand *Gyroplane Laboratoire*, 1936. *Engine:* One 350 h.p. Hispano 9Q nine-cylinder radial. *Rotor diameter (each):* 52 ft. 5⅞ in. (16·00 m.). *Fuselage length:* approx. 29 ft. 6⅓ in. (9·00 m.). *Height:* approx. 14 ft. 5¼ in. (4·40 m.). *Empty weight:* 3,153 lb. (1,430 kg.). *Take-off weight:* 4,475 lb. (2,030 kg.). *Maximum speed:* approx. 61 m.p.h. (98 km./hr.). *Endurance:* approx. 1 hr. 0 min.

Fw 61 (Germany)

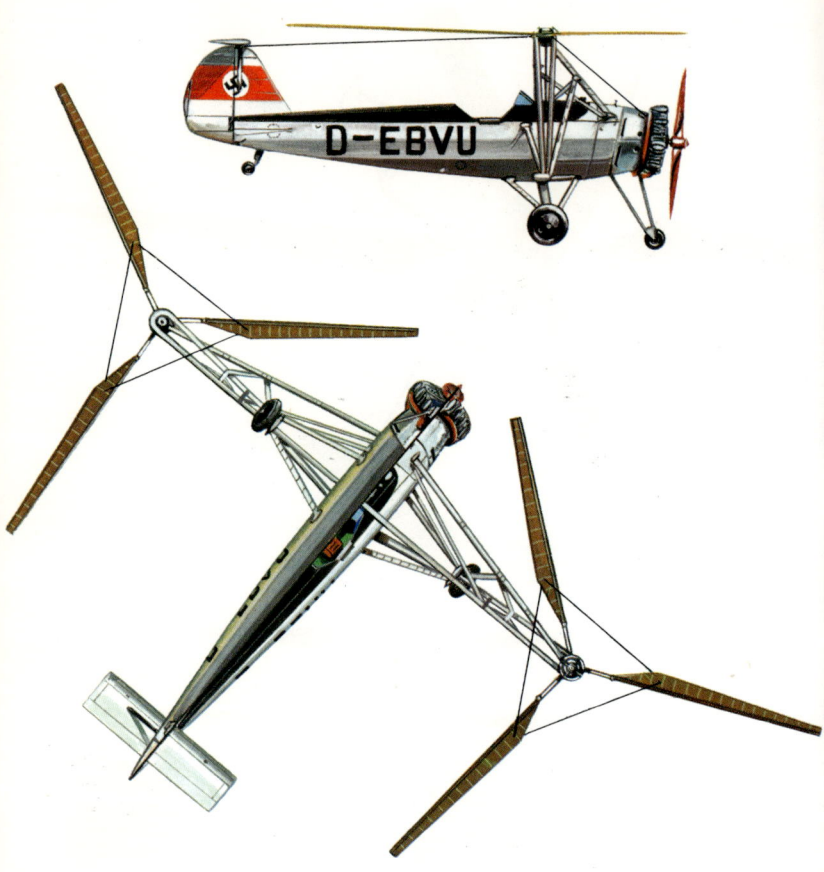

13

Focke-Wulf Fw 61 V1, 1937. *Engine:* One 160 h.p. Bramo (Siemens-Halske) Sh. 14A seven-cylinder radial. *Rotor diameter (each):* 22 ft. 11⅜ in. (7·00 m.). *Fuselage length:* 23 ft. 11 in. (7·29 m.). *Height:* approx. 8 ft. 8 in. (2·64 m.). *Maximum take-off weight:* 2,100 lb. (953 kg.). *Cruising speed:* 62 m.p.h. (100 km./hr.) at sea level. *Service ceiling:* 8,600 ft. (2,620 m.). *Range:* 143 miles (230 km.).

14

Sikorsky VS-300 in mid-1940 configuration *(top)* with 90 h.p. Franklin horizon-tally-opposed piston-engine and *(bottom)* in early 1942 configuration with 150 h.p. Franklin. *Data apply to latter version. Main rotor diameter:* 30 ft. 0 in. (9·14 m.). *Fuselage length:* 28 ft. 0 in. (8·53 m.). *Height:* 10 ft. 0 in. (3·05 m.). *Take-off weight:* 1,150 lb. (522 kg.). *Maximum speed:* approx. 50 m.p.h. (80 km./hr.) at sea level. *Range:* 75 miles (121 km.).

FI 282 (Germany)

15

Flettner FI 282 V21, as evaluated by the *Reichsluftfahrtministerium*. 1944. *Engine:* One 150 h.p. Bramo (Siemens-Halske) Sh.14A seven-cylinder radial. *Rotor diameter (each):* 39 ft. $2\frac{7}{8}$ in. (11·96 m.). *Fuselage length:* 21 ft. $6\frac{1}{4}$ in. (6·56 m.). *Height:* 7 ft. $2\frac{5}{8}$ in. (2·20 m.). *Maximum take-off weight:* 2,205 lb. (1,000 kg.). *Maximum speed:* 93 m.p.h. (150 km./hr.) at sea level. *Service ceiling:* 10,827 ft. (3,300 m.). *Normal range:* 106 miles (170 km.).

DOBLHOFF WNF 342 (Germany)

16

Doblhoff WNF 342 V4, 1945. *Engine:* One 140 h.p. Bramo (Siemens-Halske) Sh.14A seven-cylinder radial. *Rotor diameter:* 32 ft. 8⅛ in. (9·96 m.). *Fuselage length:* approx. 16 ft. 7½ in. (5·07 m.). *Height:* approx. 7 ft. 10½ in. (2·40 m.). *Maximum take-off weight:* 1,411 lb. (640 kg.). *Maximum speed:* 25 m.p.h. (40 km./hr.) at sea level.

Fa 223 (Germany)

17

One of two Focke-Achgelis Fa 223 *Drache* aircraft completed by Závody in Czechoslovakia 1945-46 from captured German components. *Engine:* One 1,000 h.p. Bramo 323 Q-3 nine-cylinder radial. *Rotor diameter (each):* 39 ft. 4½ in. (12·00 m.). *Fuselage length:* 40 ft. 2¼ in. (12·25 m.). *Height:* 15 ft. 9 in. (4·80 m.). *Take-off weight:* 9,480 lb. (4,300 kg.). *Maximum speed:* 114 m.p.h. (183 km./hr.) at sea level. *Service ceiling:* 23,294 ft. (7,100 m.). *Typical range:* 199 miles (320 km.).

18

Bratukhin Omega G-4, pre-series aircraft, 1948. *Engines:* Two 500 h.p. Ivchenko AI-26GR seven-cylinder radials. *Rotor diameter (each):* 25 ft. 3⅓ in. (7·70 m.). *Fuselage length:* approx. 28 ft. 3¾ in. (8·63 m.). *Height:* approx. 11 ft. 1 in. (3·38 m.). *Maximum take-off weight:* 6,618 lb. (3,002 kg.). *Maximum speed:* 92 m.p.h. (148 km./hr.) at sea level. *Hovering ceiling:* 7,874 ft. (2,400 m.). *Normal range:* 145 miles (233 km.).

SIKORSKY R-4(U.S.A.)

19

Sikorsky R-4B Hoverfly I of the R.A.F. Helicopter Training School, Andover, *ca.* 1945-46. *Engine:* One 180 h.p. Warner Super Scarab R-550-1 seven-cylinder radial. *Main rotor diameter:* 38 ft. 0 in. (11·58 m.). *Fuselage length:* 35 ft. 5 in. (10·80 m.). *Height:* 12 ft. 5 in. (3·78 m.). *Maximum take-off weight:* 2,535 lb. (1,150 kg.). *Maximum speed:* 75 m.p.h. (121 km./hr.) at sea level. *Service ceiling:* 8,000 ft. (2,438 m.). *Typical range:* 220 miles (322 km.).

20

Nash-Kelvinator-built R-6A Hoverfly II of No. 657 (A.O.P.) Squadron R.A.F., 1946. *Engine:* One 245 h.p. Franklin O-405-9 six-cylinder horizontally-opposed type. *Main rotor diameter:* 38 ft. 0 in. (11·58 m.). *Fuselage length:* 34 ft. 1 in. (10·39 m.). *Height:* 10 ft. 4 in. (3·15 m.). *Maximum take-off weight:* 2,590 lb. (1,175 kg.). *Maximum speed:* 96 m.p.h. (154 km./hr.) at sea level. *Service ceiling:* 10,000 ft. (3,048 m.). *Endurance:* 5 hr. 0 min.

SYCAMORE(U.K.)

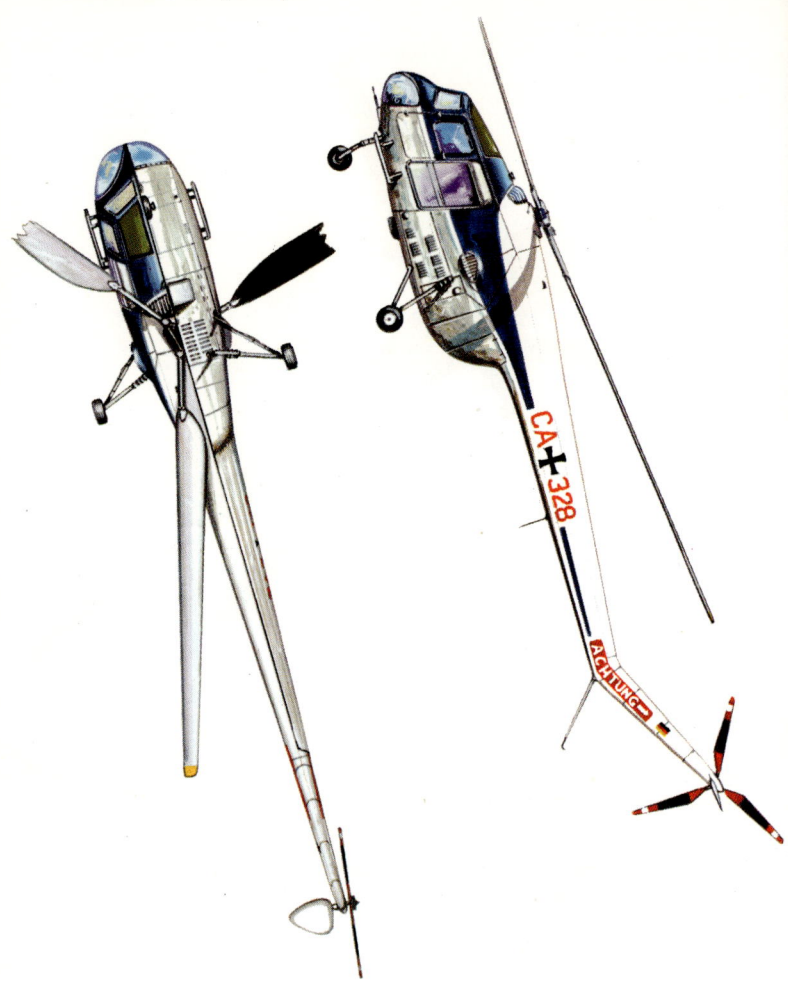

21
Bristol 171 Sycamore Mk. 52, V.I.P. Flight of the Federal German *Luftwaffe*, 1958.
Engine: One 520 h.p. Alvis Leonides 173 nine-cylinder radial. *Main rotor diameter:*
48 ft. 6¾ in. (14·80 m.). *Fuselage length:* 46 ft. 2 in. (14·07 m.). *Height:* 12 ft. 2 in.
(3·71 m.). *Maximum take-off weight:* 5,600 lb. (2,540 kg.). *Maximum speed:*
127 m.p.h. (204 km./hr.) at sea level. *Service ceiling:* 15,500 ft. (4,724 m.).
Maximum range: 268 miles (431 km.).

22

Westland WS-51 Dragonfly HR Mk. 3 of the Royal Navy, 1953. *Engine:* One 520 h.p. Alvis Leonides 50 nine-cylinder radial. *Main rotor diameter:* 49 ft. 0 in. (14·94 m.). *Fuselage length:* 40 ft. 10 in. (12·45 m.). *Height:* 12 ft. 11½ in. (3·95 m.). *Normal take-off weight:* 5,870 lb. (2,663 kg.). *Maximum speed:* 95 m.p.h. (153 km./hr.) at sea level. *Service ceiling:* 13,200 ft. (4,023 m.) *Maximum range:* 300 miles (483 km.).

DJINN (France)

23

Sud-Aviation S.O.1221 Djinn 'agricopter', June 1967. *Engine:* One 260 s.h.p.
Turboméca Palouste IV air generator, delivering 2·4 lb. (1·1 kg.) per second at
the blade tips. *Rotor diameter:* 36 ft. 1⅛ in. (11·00 m.). *Fuselage length:* 17 ft.
4⅔ in. (5·30 m.). *Height:* 8 ft. 7⅛ in. (2·62 m.). *Maximum take-off weight:* 1,675 lb
(760 kg.). *Maximum speed:* 78 m.p.h. (125 km./hr.) at sea level. *Service ceiling:*
10,170 ft. (3,100 m.). *Endurance:* 2 hr. 20 min.

24

Saunders-Roe Skeeter Mk. 51 of the Federal German *Bundesmarine.* 1959.
Engine: One 215 h.p. de Havilland Gipsy Major 215 Mk. 140 four-cylinder inverted
in-line. *Main rotor diameter:* 32 ft. 0 in. (9·75 m.). *Fuselage length:* 26 ft. 6 in.
(8·08 m.). *Height:* 7 ft. 6 in. (2·29 m.). *Normal take-off weight:* 2,200 lb. (998 kg.).
Maximum speed: 104 m.p.h. (167 km./hr.) at sea level. *Service ceiling:* 12,800 ft.
(3,900 m.). *Maximum range:* 213 miles (343 km.).

RAVEN (U.S.A.)

25

Hiller OH-23C Raven of the U.S. Army, California National Guard, 1962. *Engine:* One 200 h.p. Franklin 6V4-200-C33 six-cylinder vertically-opposed type. *Main rotor diameter:* 35 ft. 0 in. (10·67 m.). *Fuselage length:* 27 ft. 6 in. (8·38 m.). *Height:* 9 ft. 6 in. (2·90 m.). *Maximum take-off weight:* 2,500 lb. (1,134 kg.). *Maximum speed:* 87 m.p.h. (140 km./hr.) at sea level. *Service ceiling:* 10,500 ft. (3,200 m.). *Typical range:* 135 miles (217 km.).

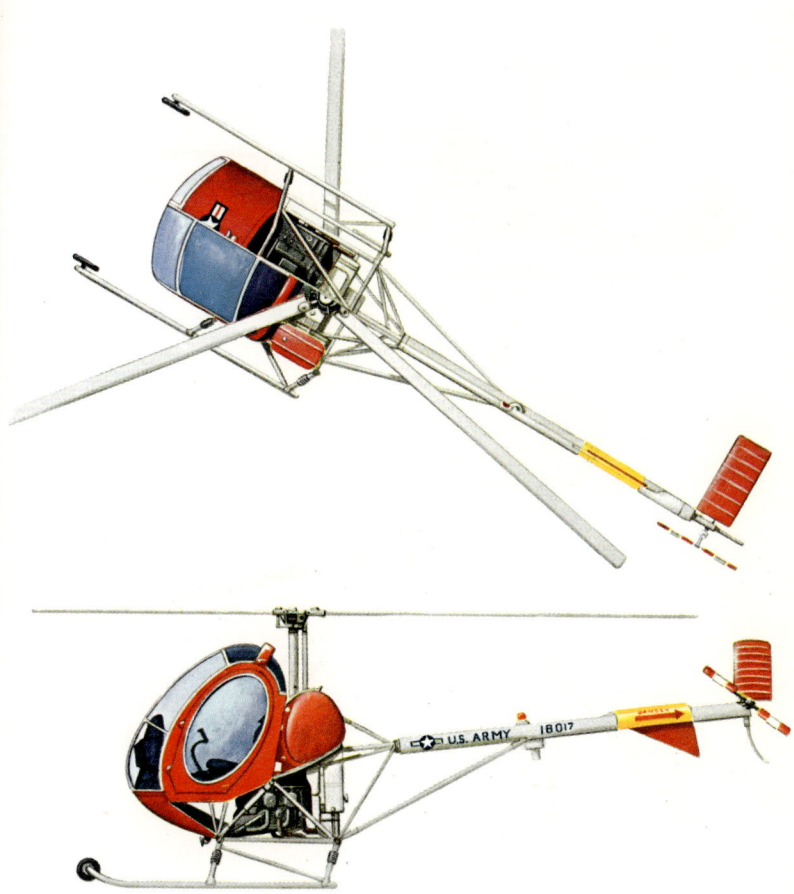

26

Hughes Model 200 (TH-55A Osage) of the U.S. Army Primary Helicopter School, Fort Wolters, Texas, 1965. *Engine:* One 180 h.p. Lycoming HIO-360-A1A four-cylinder horizontally-opposed type. *Main rotor diameter:* 25 ft. 3½ in. (7·71 m.). *Fuselage length:* 21 ft. 10¾ in. (6·67 m.). *Height:* 8 ft. 3 in. (2·51 m.). *Maximum take-off weight:* 1,600 lb. (725 kg.). *Maximum speed:* 86 m.p.h. (138 km./hr.) at sea level. *Service ceiling:* 11,500 ft. (3,500 m.). *Maximum endurance on internal fuel:* 3 hr. 20 min.

ALOUETTE II (France)

27

Saab-built S.E.3130 Alouette II (HKP 2) of the *Kungl. Svenska Armen.* 1962.
Engine: One 530 s.h.p. Turboméca Artouste IIC6 turboshaft, derated to 360 s.h.p.
Main rotor diameter: 33 ft. 5⅝ in. (10·20 m.). *Fuselage length:* 31 ft. 9⅞ in. (9·70 m.).
Height: 9 ft. 0¼ in. (2·75 m.). *Maximum take-off weight:* 3,527 lb. (1,600 kg).
Maximum speed: 115 m.p.h. (185 km./hr.) at sea level. *Service ceiling:* 7,050 ft.
(2,150 m.). *Range with maximum fuel:* 351 miles (565 km.).

28

Silvercraft SH-4 in manufacturer's livery, *ca.* 1970. *Engine:* One 235 h.p. Franklin 6A-350-D1A six-cylinder horizontally-opposed type, derated to 170 h.p. *Main rotor diameter:* 29 ft. 7½ in. (9·03 m.). *Fuselage length:* 25 ft. 1¼ in. (7·65 m.). *Height overall:* 9 ft. 9¼ in. (2·98 m.). *Maximum take-off weight:* 1,900 lb. (862 kg.). *Maximum speed:* 100 m.p.h. (161 km/hr.) at sea level. *Service ceiling:* 15,090 ft. (4,600 m.). *Maximum range:* 200 miles (320 km.).

Mi-1 (U.S.S.R.)

29

WSK-Swidnik-built SM-1WS (Mi-1) of the Soviet Air Force, 1961. *Engine:* One 575 h.p. LiT-3 (Polish-built Ivchenko AI-26V) seven-cylinder radial. *Main rotor diameter:* 47 ft. 1 in. (14·35 m.). *Fuselage length:* 39 ft. 8½ in. (12·10 m.). *Height:* 10 ft. 10 in. (3·30 m.). *Maximum take-off weight:* 5,204 lb. (2,360 kg.). *Maximum speed:* 96 m.p.h. (155 km./hr.) at sea level. *Service ceiling:* 9,843 ft. (3,000 m.). *Maximum range:* 373 miles (600 km.).

30

WSK-Swidnik (Mil) Mi-2 of the Polish Air Force, *ca.* 1970. *Engines:* Two 437 s.h.p. Isotov GTD-350 turboshafts. *Main rotor diameter:* 47 ft. 6¾ in. (14·50 m.). *Fuselage length:* 37 ft. 4¾ in. (11·40 m.). *Height:* 12 ft. 3½ in. (3·75 m.). *Maximum normal take-off weight:* 7,826 lb. (3,550 kg.). *Maximum speed:* 130 m.p.h. (210 km/hr.) at 1,640 ft. (500 m.). *Service ceiling:* 13,775 ft. (4,200 m.). *Range with maximum payload of 1,764 lb. (800 kg.):* 105 miles (170 km.).

Mi-4 (U.S.S.R.)

31

Mil Mi-4 of the Czechoslovak Air Force, *ca.* 1956. *Engine:* One 1,700 h.p. Shvetsov ASh-82V eighteen-cylinder radial. *Main rotor diameter:* 68 ft. 11 in. (21·00 m.). *Fuselage length:* 53 ft. 11 in. (16·435 m.). *Height:* 13 ft. 8¼ in. (4·17 m.). *Maximum take-off weight:* 17,196 lb. (7,800 kg.). *Maximum speed:* 130 m.p.h. (210 km./hr.) at 4,920 ft. (1,500 m.). *Service ceiling:* 18,045 ft. (5,500 m.). *Typical range:* 155 miles (250 km.).

32

Sikorsky S-55 of the Israeli Defence Force/Air Force, *ca*. 1955. *Engine:* One 600 h.p. Pratt & Whitney R-1340-57 Wasp nine-cylinder radial. *Main rotor diameter:* 49 ft. 0 in. (14·94 m.). *Fuselage length:* 42 ft. 2 in. (12·85 m.). *Height:* 13 ft. 4 in. (4·06 m.). *Maximum take-off weight:* 6,835 lb. (3,102 kg.). *Maximum speed:* 105 m.p.h. (169 km./hr.) at sea level. *Service ceiling:* 12,900 ft. (3,932 m.). *Typical range:* 440 miles (708 km.).

SIKORSKY HR2S-1 (U.S.A.)

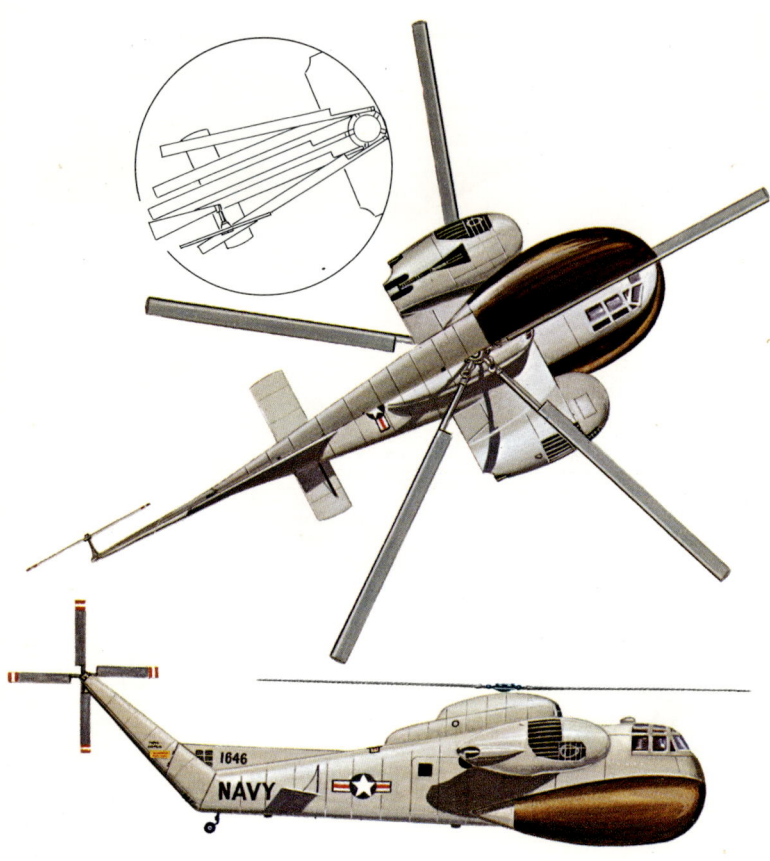

33

Sikorsky HR2S-1W of the U.S. Navy, 1958. *Engines:* Two 1,900 h.p. Pratt &
Whitney R-2800-50 Double Wasp eighteen-cylinder radials. *Main rotor diameter:*
72 ft. 0 in. (21·95 m.). *Fuselage length:* approx. 66 ft. 6 in. (20·27 m.). *Height:*
22 ft. 0¼ in. (6·71 m.). *Maximum take-off weight:* 31,000 lb. (14,061 kg.). *Maximum
speed:* 122 m.p.h. (196 km./hr.) at sea level. *Service ceiling:* 8,000 ft. (2,438 m.).
Typical range: 220 miles (354 km.).

34

Westland Whirlwind Series 3 of the Brazilian *Marinha do Guerra*, 1967. *Engine:* One 1,050 s.h.p. Rolls-Royce Gnome H.1000 turboshaft. *Main rotor diameter:* 53 ft. 0 in. (16·15 m.). *Fuselage length:* 44 ft. 2 in. (13·46 m.). *Height:* 13 ft. 2½ in. (4·03 m.). *Maximum take-off weight:* 8,000 lb. (3,629 kg.). *Maximum speed:* 106 m.p.h. (170 km./hr.) at sea level. *Service ceiling:* 10,000 ft. (3,048 m.). *Normal range:* 300 miles (483 km.).

SIKORSKY S-58 (U.S.A.)

35

Sikorsky S-58C of Sabena Belgian World Airlines, 1959. *Engine:* One 1,525 h.p. Wright R-1820-84 Cyclone nine-cylinder radial. *Main rotor diameter:* 56 ft. 0 in. (17·07 m.). *Fuselage length:* 46 ft. 9 in. (14·25 m.). *Height:* 15 ft. 10 in. (4·85 m.). *Normal take-off weight:* 13,000 lb. (5,897 kg.). *Maximum speed:* 123 m.p.h. (198 km./hr.) at sea level. *Service ceiling:* 10,500 ft. (3,200 m.). *Range with maximum fuel:* 280 miles (450 km.).

36

Westland Wessex HU Mk. 5 of No. 845 Squadron Royal Navy, 1966. *Engines:* One 1,250 s.h.p. Rolls-Royce Gnome Mk. 112 turboshaft and one 1,250 s.h.p. Gnome Mk. 113, coupled and limited to 1,550 s.h.p. at rotor head. *Main rotor diameter:* 56 ft. 0 in. (17·07 m.). *Fuselage length:* 48 ft. 4½ in. (14·74 m.). *Height:* 14 ft. 5 in. (4·39 m.). *Maximum take-off weight:* 13,500 lb. (6,124 kg.). *Maximum speed:* 132 m.p.h. (212 km./hr.) at sea level. *Service ceiling:* 14,100 ft. (4,297 m.). *Range with maximum fuel:* 478 miles (770 km.).

IROQUOIS (U.S.A.)

37

Bell UH-1B Iroquois of the U.S. Army with experimental armament of six Nord AS.11 wire-guided missiles, 1959. *Engine:* One 960 s.h.p. Lycoming T53-L-5 turboshaft. *Main rotor diameter:* 44 ft. 0 in. (13·41 m.). *Fuselage length:* 42 ft. 7 in. (12·98 m.). *Height:* 12 ft. 8½ in. (3·87 m.). *Maximum take-off weight:* 8,500 lb. (3,856 kg.). *Maximum speed:* 138 m.p.h. (222 km./hr.) at sea level. *Service ceiling:* 14,000 ft. (4,267 m.). *Typical range:* 230 miles (370 km.).

38

Agusta-Bell 204B of the *Esercito Italiano,* 1968. *Engine:* One 1,100 s.h.p. Lycoming T53-L-11A turboshaft. *Main rotor diameter:* 48 ft. 0 in. (14·63 m.). *Fuselage length:* 44 ft. 7 in. (13·59 m.). *Height:* 12 ft. 8½ in. (3·87 m.). *Normal take-off weight:* 8,500 lb. (3,856 kg.). *Maximum speed:* 138 m.p.h. (222 km./hr.) at sea level. *Service ceiling:* 15,800 ft. (4,816 m.). *Maximum range:* 380 miles (612 km.).

AGUSTA A 106 (Italy)

39

Agusta A 106 of the *Marinavia Italiana* during trials on board the Italian Navy ship *Intrepido*, 1972. *Engine:* One 354 s.h.p. Turboméca-Agusta TM-251 turboshaft, derated to 330 s.h.p. *Main rotor diameter:* 31 ft. 2 in. (9·50 m.). *Length overall:* 36 ft. 0 in. (10·975 m.). *Height:* 8 ft. 2½ in. (2·50 m.). *Maximum take-off weight:* 3,086 lb. (1,400 kg.). *Maximum speed:* 110 m.p.h. (177 km./hr.) at sea level. *Hovering ceiling in ground effect:* 8,350 ft. (2,545 m.). *Normal range:* 155 miles (250 km.).

40

Hughes Model 500 of the Australian National Antarctic Research Expedition, 1971. *Engine:* One 317 s.h.p. Allison 250-C18A turboshaft, derated to 278 s.h.p. *Main rotor diameter:* 26 ft. 4 in. (8·03 m.). *Fuselage length:* 23 ft. 0 in. (7·01 m.). *Height:* 8 ft. 1½ in. (2·48 m.). *Maximum normal take-off weight:* 2,550 lb. (1,157 kg.). *Maximum speed:* 152 m.p.h. (244 km./hr.) at 1,000 ft. (305 m.). *Service ceiling:* 14,400 ft. (4,390 m.). *Range:* 377 miles (606 km.).

LYNX (U.K. /France)

41

Westland/Aérospatiale Lynx, first prototype, spring 1971. *Data apply to AH Mk. 1 production version. Engines:* Two 830 s.h.p. Rolls-Royce BS.360-07-26 turbo-shafts. *Main rotor diameter:* 42 ft. 0 in. (12·80 m.). *Fuselage length:* 38 ft. 3¼ in. (11·665 m.). *Height overall:* 11 ft. 3 in. (3·43 m.). *Maximum take-off weight:* 8.000 lb. (3,628 kg.). *Maximum cruising speed:* 184 m.p.h. (296 km/hr.) at sea level. *Hovering ceiling out of ground effect:* 12,000 ft. (3,650 m.). *Typical range:* 489 miles (788 km.).

42

Agusta-Bell 206A JetRanger of the Swedish Police Department, *ca.* 1971. *Engine:* One 317 s.h.p. Allison 250-C18 turboshaft. *Main rotor diameter:* 33 ft. 4 in. (10·16 m.). *Fuselage length:* 31 ft. 2 in. (9·50 m.). *Height:* 9 ft. 6½ in. (2·91 m.). *Maximum take-off weight:* 3,000 lb. (1,360 kg.). *Maximum speed:* 150 m.p.h. (241 km./hr.) at sea level. *Service ceiling:* over 17,000 ft. (5,182 m.). *Maximum range:* 391 miles (629 km.).

HUEYCOBRA (U.S.A.)

43

Bell AH-1G HueyCobra of the U.S. Army, 1967, armed with two XM-159 launchers each with nineteen 2·75 in. FFAR rockets. *Engine:* One 1,400 s.h.p. Lycoming T53-L-13 turboshaft, derated to 1,100 s.h.p. *Main rotor diameter:* 44 ft. 0 in. (13·41 m.). *Fuselage length:* 44 ft. 5¼ in. (13·54 m.). *Height:* 13 ft. 5½ in. (4·10 m.). *Maximum take-off weight:* 9,500 lb. (4,309 kg.). *Maximum cruising speed:* 196 m.p.h. (315 km./hr.) at sea level. *Service ceiling:* 11,400 ft. (3,475 m.). *Typical range:* 230 miles (370 km.).

44

Sikorsky S-67 Blackhawk prototype, 1972. *Engines:* Two 1,500 s.h.p. General Electric T58-GE-5 turboshafts. *Main rotor diameter:* 62 ft. 0 in. (18·90 m.). *Wing span:* 27 ft. 4 in. 8·33 m.). *Fuselage length:* 64 ft. 9 in. (19·74 m.). *Height:* 15 ft. 0 in. (4·57 m.). *Maximum take-off weight:* 24,400 lb. (11,067 kg.). *Maximum speed:* 203 m.p.h. (327 km /hr.) at sea level. *Service ceiling:* 17,000 ft. (5,180 m.). *Maximum range:* 1,122 miles (1,805 km.).

45

Bell Model 309 KingCobra, second prototype, 1972. *Engine:* One 2,050 s.h.p. Lycoming T55-L-7C turboshaft. *Main rotor diameter:* 48 ft. 0 in. (14·63 m.). *Wing span:* 13 ft. 0 in. (3·96 m.). *Fuselage length:* 49 ft. 0 in. (14·93 m.). *Maximum take-off weight:* 14,000 lb. (6,350 kg.). *Maximum speed:* approx 230 m.p.h. (370 km./hr.). *Hovering ceiling out of ground effect:* 4,000 ft. (1,220 m.).

46

Lockheed AH-56A Cheyenne prototype in U.S. Army finish, 1972. *Engine:* One 3,925 s.h.p. General Electric T64-GE-16 turboshaft. *Main rotor diameter:* 51 ft. 3 in. (15·62 m.). *Wing span:* 26 ft. 8½ in. (8·14 m.). *Fuselage length:* 54 ft. 8 in. (16·66 m.). *Height:* 13 ft. 8½ in. (4·18 m.). *Maximum take-off weight:* 18,300 lb. (8,301 kg.). *Maximum speed:* 244 m.p.h. (393 km./hr.) at sea level. *Service ceiling:* 20,000 ft. (6.100 m.). *Maximum range (ferry):* 1,225 miles (1,971 km.).

SIKORSKY S-61 and SEA KING (U.S.A.)

47
Sikorsky S-61A-1 of No. 722 Squadron, Royal Danish *Flyvevåbnet:* individual winner of air/sea rescue competition for the Henri Dunant trophy, August 1967. *Engines:* Two 1,250 s.h.p. General Electric T58-GE-8B turboshafts. *Main rotor dia-*

meter: 62 ft. 0 in. (18·90 m.). *Fuselage length:* 54 ft. 9 in. (16·69 m.). *Height:* 16 ft. 10 in. (5·13 m.). *Normal take-off weight:* 20,500 lb. (9,299 kg.). *Maximum speed:* 166 m.p.h. (267 km./hr.) at sea level. *Service ceiling:* 14,700 ft. (4,480 m.). *Range with maximum fuel:* 625 miles (1,006 km.).

50

Westland Sea King HAS Mk. 1 of No. 700 (S) Squadron Royal Navy, R.N.A.S. Culdrose, 1970. *Engines:* Two 1,500 s.h.p. Rolls-Royce Bristol Gnome H.1400 turboshafts. *Main rotor diameter:* 62 ft. 0 in. (18·90 m.). *Fuselage length:* 55 ft. 9¾ in. (17·01 m.). *Height:* 15 ft. 6 in. (4·72 m.). *Maximum take-off weight:* 20,500 lb. (9,299 kg.). *Normal operating speed (ASW):* 131 m.p.h. (211 km./hr.). *Approved ceiling:* 10,000 ft. (3,050 m.). *Typical range, standard fuel:* 598 miles (963 km.).

48

Sikorsky SH-3A Sea King of the Japan Maritime Self-Defence Force, *ca*. 1964. Data similar to those for S-61A.

49

Agusta - Sikorsky SH - 3D of the *Marinavia Italiana,* 1971. *Engines:* Two 1,400 s.h.p. General Electric T58-GE-10 turboshafts. *Normal take-off weight:* 18,626 lb. (8,449 kg.). Other data similar to those for S-61A.

SIKORSKY S-61N (U.S.A.)

51

Sikorsky S-61N of BEA Helicopters Ltd., *ca.* 1968. *Engines:* Two 1,500 s.h.p. General Electric CT58-140-2 turboshafts. *Main rotor diameter:* 62 ft. 0 in. (18·90 m.). *Fuselage length:* 59 ft. 4 in. (18·08 m.). *Height:* 17 ft. 5½ in. (5·32 m.). *Maximum take-off weight:* 19,000 lb. (8,618 kg.). *Maximum speed:* 150 m.p.h. (241 km./hr.) at sea level. *Service ceiling:* 12,200 ft. (3,720 m.). *Range with maximum fuel:* 450 miles (724 km.).

SIKORSKY S-62A (U.S.A.)

52

Mitsubishi-built Sikorsky S-62A in manufacturer's livery, 1964. *Engine:* One 1,250 s.h.p. General Electric CT58-110-1 turboshaft, derated to 730 s.h.p. *Main rotor diameter:* 53 ft. 0 in. (16·16 m.). *Fuselage length:* 44 ft. 6½ in. (13·58 m.). *Height:* 14 ft. 2½ in. (4·33 m.). *Maximum take-off weight:* 7,900 lb. (3,583 kg.). *Maximum speed:* 101 m.p.h. (163 km./hr.) at sea level. *Service ceiling:* 6,600 ft. (2,010 m.). *Range on internal fuel:* 462 miles (743 km.).

SCOUT (U.K.)

53

Westland Scout of the Uganda Police Department, 1966. *Engine:* One 968 s.h.p. Rolls-Royce Nimbus 101 turboshaft, derated to 685 s.h.p. *Main rotor diameter:* 32 ft. 3 in. (9·83 m.). *Fuselage length:* 30 ft. 4 in. (9·24 m.). *Height:* 8 ft. 11 in. (2·72 m.). *Maximum take-off weight:* 5,300 lb. (2,404 kg.). *Maximum speed:* 131 m.p.h. (211 km./hr.) at sea level. *Service ceiling:* 13,400 ft. (4,085 m.). *Range with maximum fuel:* 315 miles (507 km.).

54

Bell 47G of the Sheriff's Department,
County of Los Angeles, California, 1961.
Engine: One 200 h.p. Franklin 6V4-200-
C32 six-cylinder vertically-opposed type.
Main rotor diameter: 35 ft. 1½ in. (10·71 m.).
Fuselage length: 31 ft. 7 in. (9·62 m.).
Height: 9 ft. 3¾ in. (2·84 m.). *Maximum
take-off weight:* 2,350 lb. (1,066 kg.).
Maximum speed: 100 m.p.h. (161 km./hr.)
at sea level. *Service ceiling:* 10,900 ft.
(3,322 m.). *Range:* 215 miles (346 km.).

55

Agusta-Bell 47J-2A owned by Ferranti Ltd., 1967. *Engine:* One 305 h.p. Lycoming
VO-540-B1B six-cylinder horizontally-opposed (vertically-mounted) type, derated to 260 h.p. *Main rotor diameter:* 37 ft. 2 in. (11·33 m.). *Fuselage length:*
32 ft. 4¾ in. (13·20 m.). *Height:* 9 ft. 3½ in. (2·83 m.). *Maximum take-off weight:*
2,950 lb. (1,338 kg.). *Maximum speed:* 105 m.p.h. (169 km./hr.) at sea level.
Service ceiling: 11,000 ft. (3,353 m.). *Maximum range:* 258 miles (415 km.).

ALOUETTE III (France)

56

Aérospatiale SA 316C Alouette III of the Yugoslav Air Force, 1972. *Engine:* One 870 s.h.p. Turboméca Artouste IIID turboshaft, derated to 600 s.h.p. *Main rotor diameter:* 36 ft. 1¾ in. (11·02 m.). *Fuselage length:* 33 ft. 4⅜ in. (10·17 m.). *Height:* 9 ft. 10⅛ in. (3·00 m.). *Maximum take-off weight:* 4,960 lb. (2,250 kg.). *Maximum speed:* 136 m.p.h. (220 km./hr.) at sea level. *Service ceiling:* 13,125 ft. (4,000 m.). *Range at sea level with maximum fuel:* 298 miles (480 km.).

57

Aérospatiale/Westland SA 341 Gazelle, third pre-production aircraft in British Army finish, 1971. *Engine:* One 590 s.h.p. Turboméca Astazou III turboshaft. *Main rotor diameter:* 34 ft. 5½ in. (10·50 m.). *Fuselage length:* 31 ft. 2¾ in. (9·52 m.). *Height:* 9 ft. 0¼ in. (2·75 m.). *Maximum take-off weight:* 3,747 lb. (1,700 kg.). *Maximum cruising speed:* 160 m.p.h. (257 km./hr.) at sea level. *Service ceiling:* 15,100 ft. (4,600 m.). *Range at sea level with maximum fuel:* 416 miles (670 km.).

BO 105 (W. Germany)

58

MBB BO 105 of the Federal German police force, early 1972. *Engines:* Two 400 s.h.p. Allison 250-C20 turboshafts, each derated to 317 s.h.p. *Main rotor diameter:* 32 ft. 2¾ in. (9·82 m.). *Fuselage length:* 28 ft. 0½ in. (8·55 m.). *Height:* 9 ft. 9⅜ in. (2·98 m.). *Normal take-off weight:* 4,629 lb. (2,100 kg.). *Maximum cruising speed:* 138 m.p.h. (222 km./hr.) at sea level. *Service ceiling:* 13,450 ft. (4,100 m.). *Normal range:* 388 miles (625 km.).

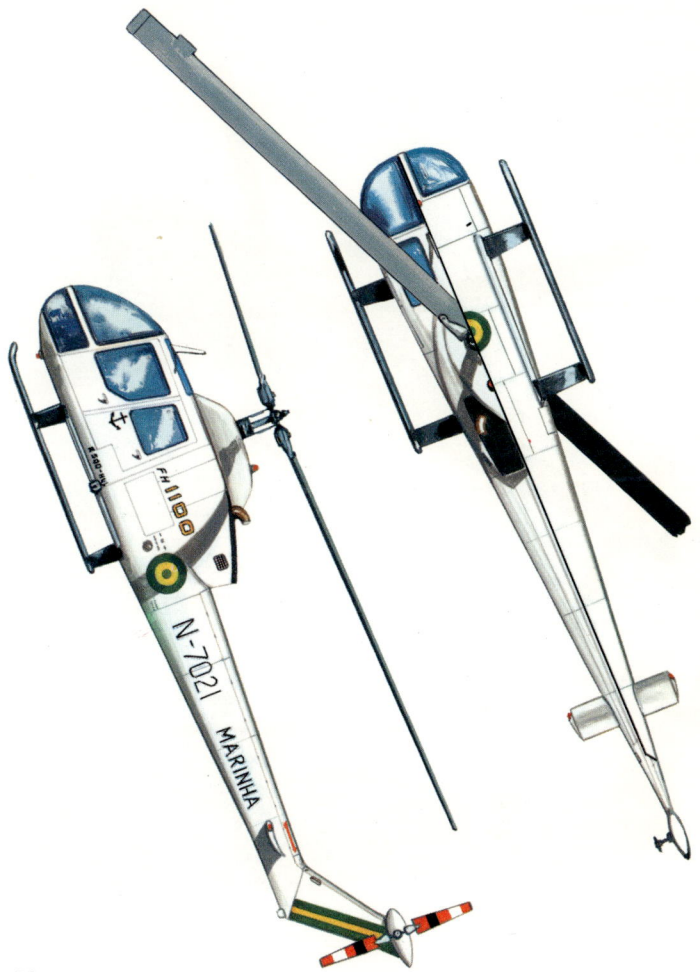

59

Fairchild Industries FH-1100 of the Brazilian *Marinha do Guerra. ca.* 1970-71.
Engine: One 317 s.h.p. Allison 250-C18 turboshaft, derated to 274 s.h.p. *Main rotor diameter:* 35 ft. 4¾ in. (10·79 m.). *Fuselage length:* 29 ft. 9½ in. (9·08 m.).
Height: 9 ft. 3½ in. (2·83 m.). *Maximum take-off weight:* 2,750 lb. (1,247 kg.).
Maximum cruising speed: 127 m.p.h. (240 km./hr.) at 5,000 ft. (1,525 m.). *Service ceiling:* 14,200 ft. (4,325 m.). *Range with maximum payload:* 348 miles (560 km.).

SEASPRITE (U.S.A.)

60

Kaman SH-2D Seasprite of the U.S. Navy, late 1971. *Engines:* Two 1,350 s.h.p. General Electric T58-GE-8F turboshafts. *Main rotor diameter:* 44 ft. 0 in. (13·41 m.). *Fuselage length:* 40 ft. 6 in. (12·34 m.). *Height to top of rotor hub:* 13 ft. 7 in. (4·14 m.). *Normal take-off weight:* 12,500 lb. (5,670 kg.). *Maximum speed:* 168 m.p.h. (270 km./hr.) at sea level. *Service ceiling:* 22,500 ft. (6,858 m.). *Normal range:* 445 miles (716 km.).

61

Aérospatiale/Westland SA 330E Puma HC Mk. 1 of No. 33 Squadron R.A.F., 1971. *Engines:* Two 1,328 s.h.p. Turboméca Turmo IIIC4 turboshafts. *Main rotor diameter:* 49 ft. 2½ in. (15·00 m.) *Fuselage length:* 46 ft. 1½ in. (14·06 m.). *Height:* 14 ft. 4½ in. (4·38 m.). *Maximum take-off weight:* 14,770 lb. (6,700 kg.). *Maximum cruising speed:* 169 m.p.h. (272 km./hr.) at sea level. *Service ceiling:* 15,100 ft. (4,600 m.). *Maximum range:* 385 miles (620 km.).

HIRUNDO (Italy)

62

Agusta A 109 Hirundo, first prototype, 1971. *Engines:* Two 400 s.h.p. Allison 250-C20 turboshafts. *Main rotor diameter:* 36 ft. 1 in. (11·00 m.). *Fuselage length:* 36 ft. 0¾ in. (10·99 m.). *Height overall:* 10 ft. 6 in. (3·20 m.). *Maximum take-off weight:* 5,070 lb. (2,300 kg.). *Maximum speed:* 172 m.p.h. (277 km./hr.) at sea level. *Service ceiling:* 8,850 ft. (2,700 m.). *Maximum range:* 457 miles (735 km.).

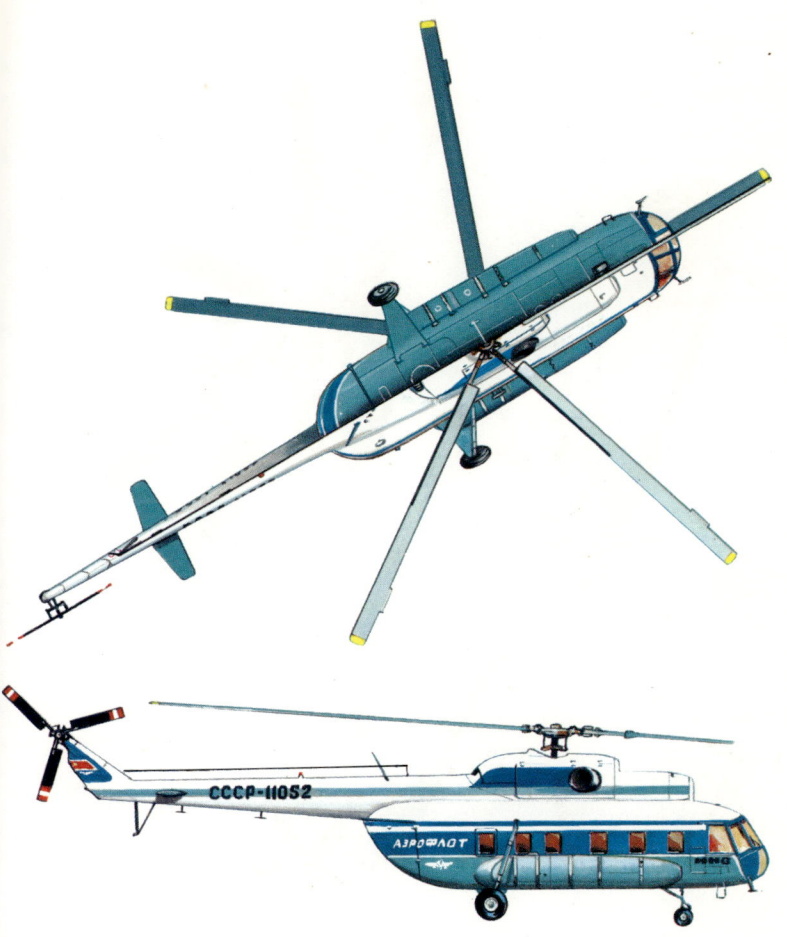

63

Mil Mi-8 of Aeroflot, June 1969. *Engines:* Two 1,700 s.h.p. Isotov TV2-117A turboshafts. *Main rotor diameter:* 69 ft. 10¼ in. (21·29 m.). *Fuse age length:* 59 ft. 7¼ in. (18·17 m.). *Height:* 14 ft. 4½ in. (4·38 m.). *Maximum vertical take-off weight:* 26,455 lb. (12,000 kg.). *Maximum speed:* 137 m.p.h. (220 km./hr.) at sea level. *Service ceiling:* 14,765 ft. (4,500 m.). *Range with 5,512 lb. (2,500 kg.) payload:* 295 miles (475 km.).

SUPER FRELON (France)

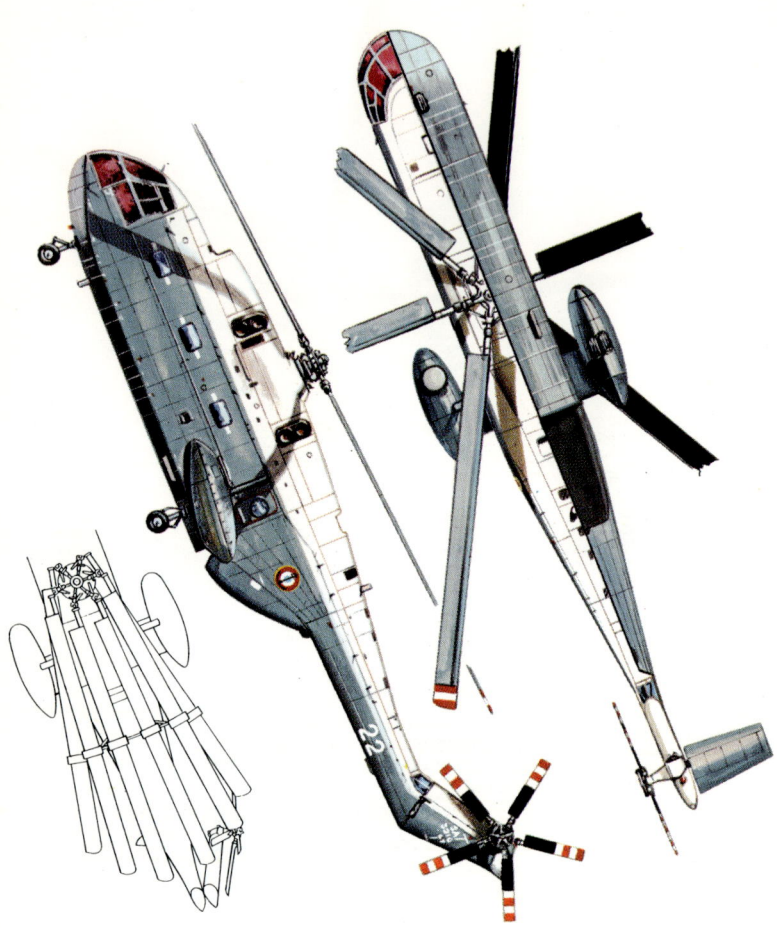

64

Aérospatiale SA 321G Super Frelon of Flottille 32F, *l'Aéronavale* (ASW configuration), 1970. *Engines:* Three 1,630 s.h.p. Turboméca Turmo IIIC6-70 turboshafts. *Main rotor diameter:* 62 ft. 0⅛ in. (18·90 m.). *Fuselage length:* 63 ft. 7¾ in. (19·40 m.). *Height:* 21 ft. 10¼ in. (6·66 m.). *Maximum take-off weight:* 28,660 lb. (13,000 kg.). *Maximum cruising speed:* 155 m.p.h. (249 km./hr.) at sea level. *Service ceiling:* 10,325 ft. (3,150 m.). *Endurance:* 4 hr. 0 min.

65

Sikorsky CII-54A, pre-series aircraft of the U.S. Army, 1965. *Data apply to production version. Engines:* Two 4,500 s.h.p. Pratt & Whitney T73-P-1 turboshafts. *Main rotor diameter:* 72 ft. 0 in. (21·95 m.). *Fuselage length:* 70 ft. 3 in. (21·41 m.). *Height:* 18 ft. 7 in. (5·67 m.). *Maximum take-off weight:* 42,000 lb. (19,050 kg.). *Maximum speed:* 127 m.p.h. (204 km./hr.) at sea level. *Service ceiling:* 13,000 ft. (3,962 m.). *Range with maximum fuel:* 253 miles (407 km.).

Mi-10 (U.S.S.R.)

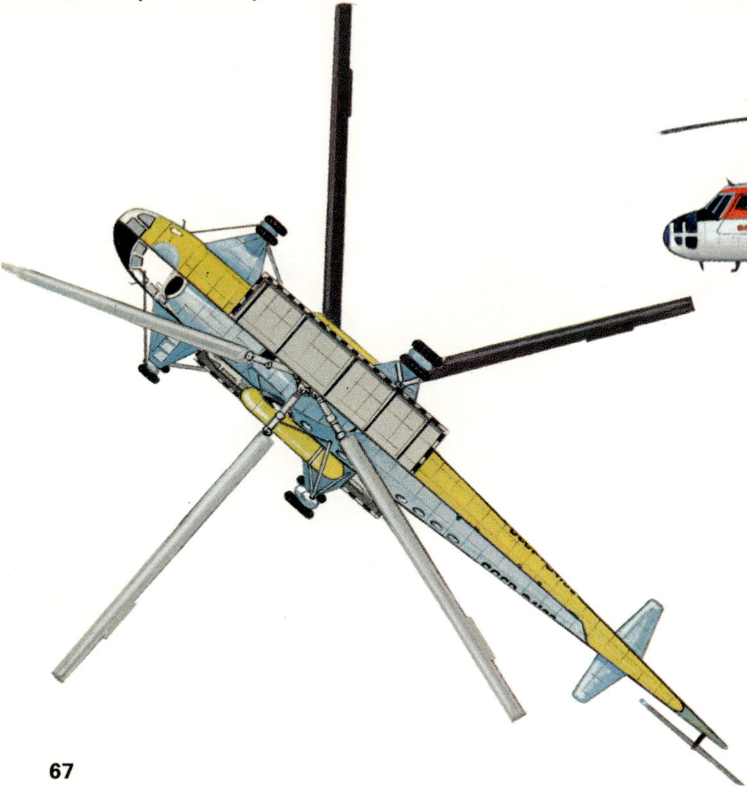

67

Mil Mi-10 in demonstration finish, 1965. *Engines:* Two 5,500 s.h.p. Soloviev D-25V turboshafts. *Main rotor diameter:* 114 ft. 10 in. (35·00 m.). *Fuselage length:* 107 ft. 9¾ in. (32·86 m.). *Height:* 32 ft. 2 in. (9·80 m.). *Maximum take-off weight:* 96,340 lb. (43,700 kg.). *Maximum speed:* 124 m.p.h. (200 km./hr.) at sea level. *Service ceiling (limited):* 9,843 ft. (3,000 m.). *Normal range:* 155 miles (250 km.).

Mi-6 (U.S.S.R.)

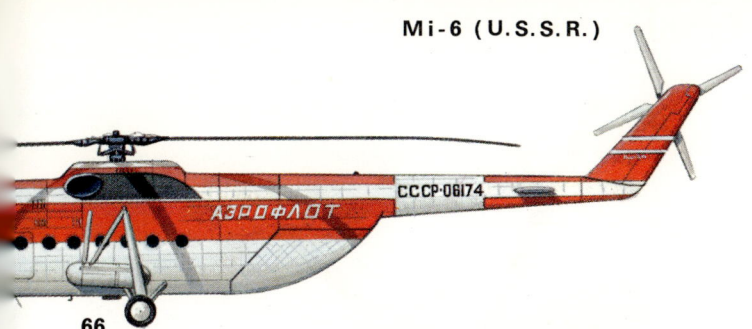

66

Mil Mi-6 of Aeroflot, as displayed at Le Bourget, June 1967. *Engines:* Two 5,500 s.h.p. Soloviev D-25V turboshafts. *Main rotor diameter:* 114 ft. 10 in. (35·00 m.). *Fuselage length:* 108 ft. 10½ in. (33·18 m.). *Height:* 32 ft. 4 in. (9·86 m.). *Maximum vertical take-off weight:* 93,696 lb. (42,500 kg.). *Maximum speed:* 186 m.p.h. (300 km./hr.) at sea level. *Service ceiling:* 14,764 ft. (4,500 m.). *Range with 13,228 lb. (6,000 kg.) payload:* 404 miles (650 km.).

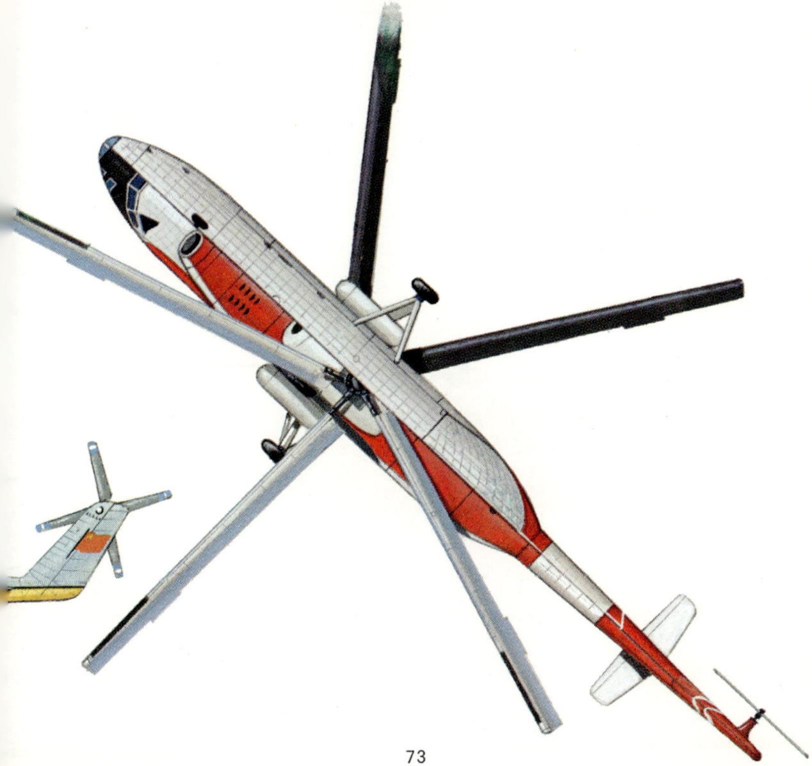

SIKORSKY HH-3 (U.S.A.)

68

Sikorsky HH-3E of the U.S.A.F. Aerospace Rescue and Recovery Service in Southeast Asia camouflage, 1967. (One of two aircraft to make the first non-stop Atlantic crossing by helicopter.) *Engines:* Two 1,500 s.h.p. General Electric T58-GE-5 turboshafts. *Main rotor diameter:* 62 ft. 0 in. (18·90 m.). *Fuselage length:* 57 ft. 3 in. (17·45 m.). *Height:* 18 ft. 1 in. (5·51 m.). *Maximum take-off weight:* 22,050 lb. (10,002 kg.). *Maximum speed:* 162 m.p.h. (261 km/hr.) at sea level. *Service ceiling:* 11,100 ft. (3,385 m.). *Range:* 465 miles (748 km.).

69

Sikorsky CH-53A Sea Stallion of the U.S. Marine Corps, 1967. *Engines:* Two 2,850 s.h.p. General Electric T64-GE-6 turboshafts. *Main rotor diameter:* 72 ft. 3 in. (22·02 m.). *Fuselage length:* 67 ft. 2 in. (20·47 m.). *Height:* 17 ft. 1½ in. (5·22 m.). *Normal take-off weight:* 35,000 lb. (15,875 kg.). *Maximum speed:* 195 m.p.h. (314 km./hr.) at sea level. *Service ceiling:* 18,550 ft. (5,654 m.). *Range:* 258 miles (415 km.).

BENSEN GYRO-COPTER (U.S.A.)

WALLIS WA-116 (U.K.)

70

Bensen B-8M Gyro-Copter owned by Mr. Vernon Bibb, 1965. *Engine:* One 72 h.p. McCulloch 4318E four-cylinder horizontally-opposed type. *Rotor diameter:* 20 ft. 0 in. (6·10 m.). *Fuselage length:* 11 ft. 3 in. (3·43 m.). *Height:* 6 ft. 3 in. (1·90 m.). *Maximum take-off weight:* 500 lb. (227 kg.). *Maximum speed:* 85 m.p.h. (137 km./hr.) at sea level. *Service ceiling:* 16,500 ft. (5,030 m.). *Normal range:* 100 miles (161 km.).

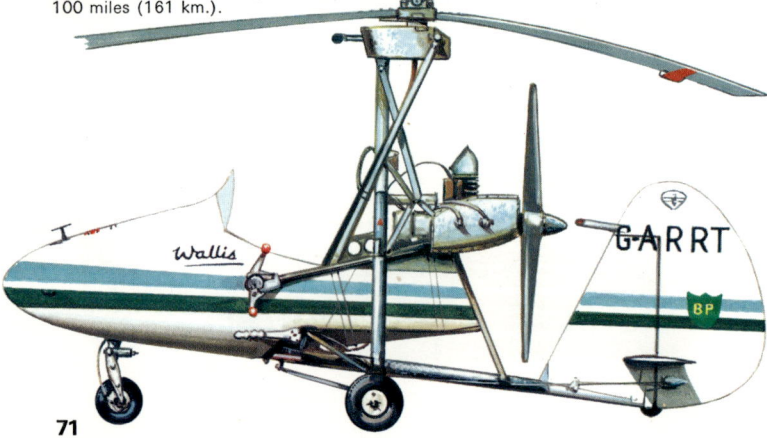

71

Wallis WA-116, 1972. *Engine:* One 100 h.p. (approx.) Wallis-McCulloch four-cylinder horizontally-opposed type. *Rotor diameter:* 20 ft. 2 in. (6·15 m.). *Fuselage length:* 11 ft. 1 in. (3·38 m.). *Height:* 6 ft. 1 in. (1·85 m.). *Maximum certificated take-off weight:* 550 lb. (250 kg.). *Maximum speed* 130 m.p.h. (209 km./hr.) at sea level. *Service ceiling:* over 15,000 ft. (4,575 m.). *Normal maximum range:* 140 miles (225 km.).

KOLIBRIE (Netherlands)

SKY-TRAC (W. Germany)

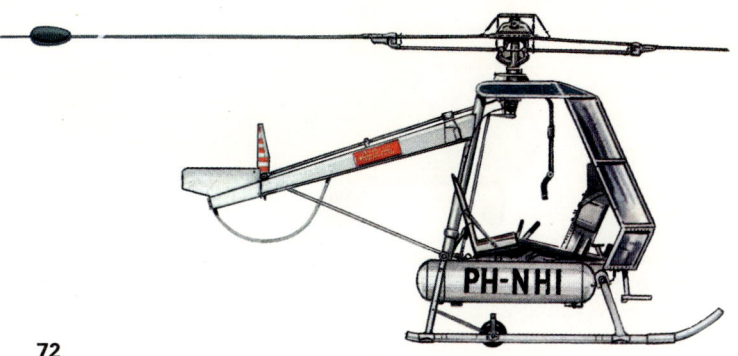

72

N.H.I. H-3 Kolibrie in manufacturer's demonstration finish, 1957. *Engines:* Two 44 lb. (20 kg.) s.t. TJ-5 ramjets. *Main rotor diameter:* 32 ft. 9¾ in. (10·00 m.). *Fuselage length:* 13 ft. 10⅛ in. (4·22 m.). *Height:* 8 ft. 6 in. (2·59 m.). *Maximum take-off weight:* 1,433 lb. (650 kg.). *Maximum speed:* 70 m.p.h. (113 km./hr.) at sea level. *Range:* 43 miles (70 km.) as single-seater.

73

Wagner Sky-Trac 3 prototype in manufacturer's demonstration finish, 1966 *Engine:* One 260 h.p. Franklin 6AS-335-B six-cylinder horizontally-opposed type. *Rotor diameter (each):* 32 ft. 9¾ in. (10·00 m.). *Fuselage length:* 13 ft. 1½ in. (4·00 m.). *Height:* 12 ft. 5½ in. (3·80 m.). *Maximum take-off weight:* 3,307 lb. (1,500 kg.). *Maximum speed:* 103 m.p.h. (166 km./hr.) at sea level. *Service ceiling:* 7,218 ft. (2,200 m.). *Maximum range:* 124 miles (200 km.).

Ka-15 and Ka-18 (U.S.S.R.)

74

Kamov Ka-15, probably an evaluation aircraft, in Soviet military markings *ca.* 1956. *Engine:* One 255 h.p. Ivchenko AI-14V nine-cylinder radial. *Rotor diameter (each):* 32 ft. 8¼ in. (9·96 m.). *Fuselage length:* 20 ft. 5¼ in. (6·23 m.). *Height:* 11 ft. 0 in. (3·35 m.). *Maximum take-off weight:* 3,148 lb. (1,428 kg.). *Maximum speed:* 93 m.p.h. (150 km./hr.) at sea level. *Service ceiling:* 9,843 ft. (3,000 m.). *Range on internal fuel:* 193 miles (310 km.).

75

Kamov Ka-18 evaluation aircraft in Soviet Air Force colours, early 1958. *Engine:* One 255 h.p. Ivchenko AI-14V nine-cylinder radial. *Rotor diameter (each):* 32 ft. 8¼ in. (9·96 m.). *Fuselage length:* 23 ft. 0¾ in. (7·03 m.). *Height:* 11 ft. 0 in. (3·35 m.). *Maximum take-off weight:* 3,263 lb. (1,480 kg.). *Maximum cruising speed:* 81 m.p.h. (130 km./hr.) at 1,640 ft. (500 m.). *Service ceiling:* 9,843 ft. (3,000 m.). *Range with maximum fuel:* 214 miles (345 km.).

76

Kamov Ka-25 of the Soviet Navy, *ca.* 1970-71. Data generally similar to those for Ka-25K below.

77

Kamov Ka-25K in Aeroflot colours, June 1967. *Engines:* Two 900 s.h.p. Glushenkov GTD-3 turboshafts. *Rotor diameter (each):* 51 ft. 8 in. (15·74 m.). *Fuselage length:* 32 ft. 3 in. (9·83 m.). *Height:* 17 ft. 7$\frac{1}{2}$ in. (5·37 m.). *Maximum take-off weight:* 16,094 lb. (7,300 kg.). *Maximum speed:* 137 m.p.h. (220 km./hr.) at sea level. *Service ceiling:* 11,483 ft. (3,500 m.). *Normal range:* 249 miles (400 km.).

HUSKIE (U.S.A.)

78

Kaman HH-43B Huskie of the U.S. Air Force, Southeast Asia, 1967. *Engine:* One 860 s.h.p. Lycoming T53 - L - 1B turbo-shaft, derated to 825 s.h.p. *Rotor diameter (each):* 47 ft. 0 in. (14·33 m.). *Fuselage length:* 25 ft. 2 in. (7·67 m.). *Height:* 12 ft. 7 in. (3·84 m.). *Maximum take-off weight:* 7,100 lb. (3,220 kg.). *Maximum speed:* 120 m.p.h. (193 km./hr.) at sea level. *Service ceiling:* 25,000 ft. (7,620 m.). *Range on internal fuel:* 277 miles (445 km.).

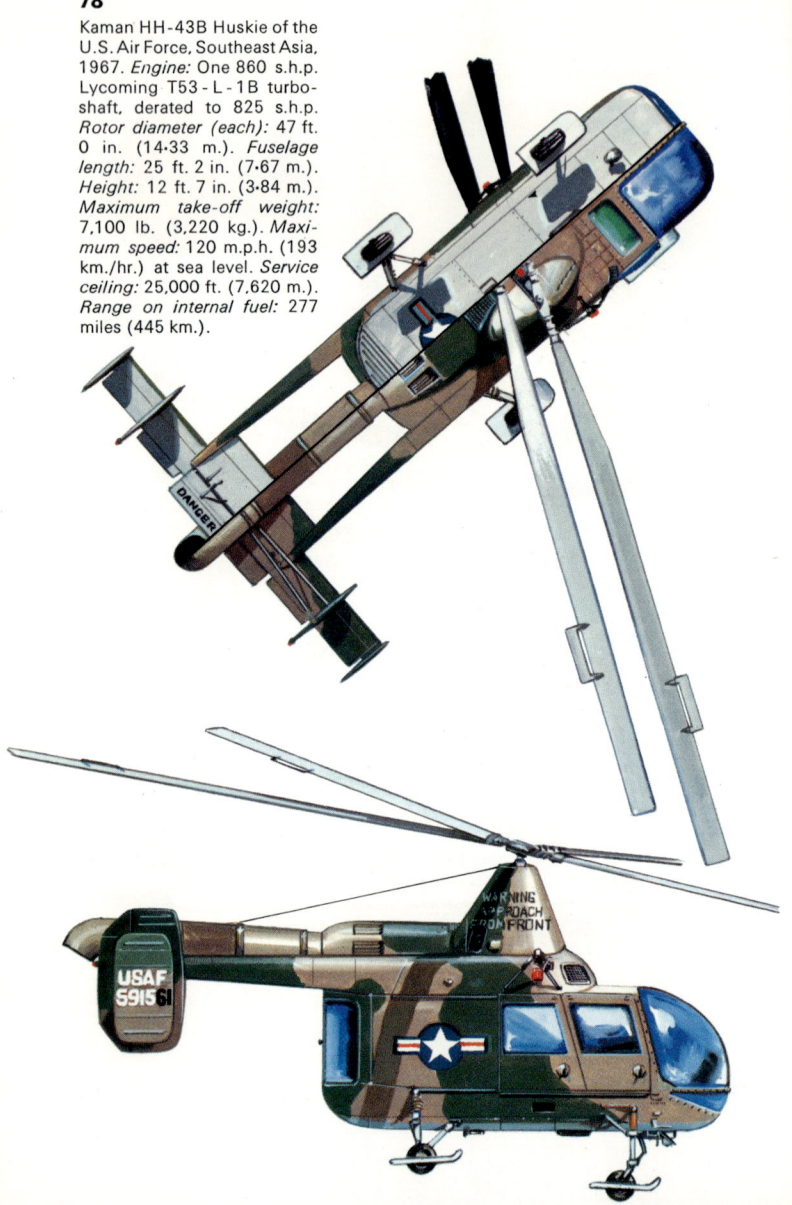

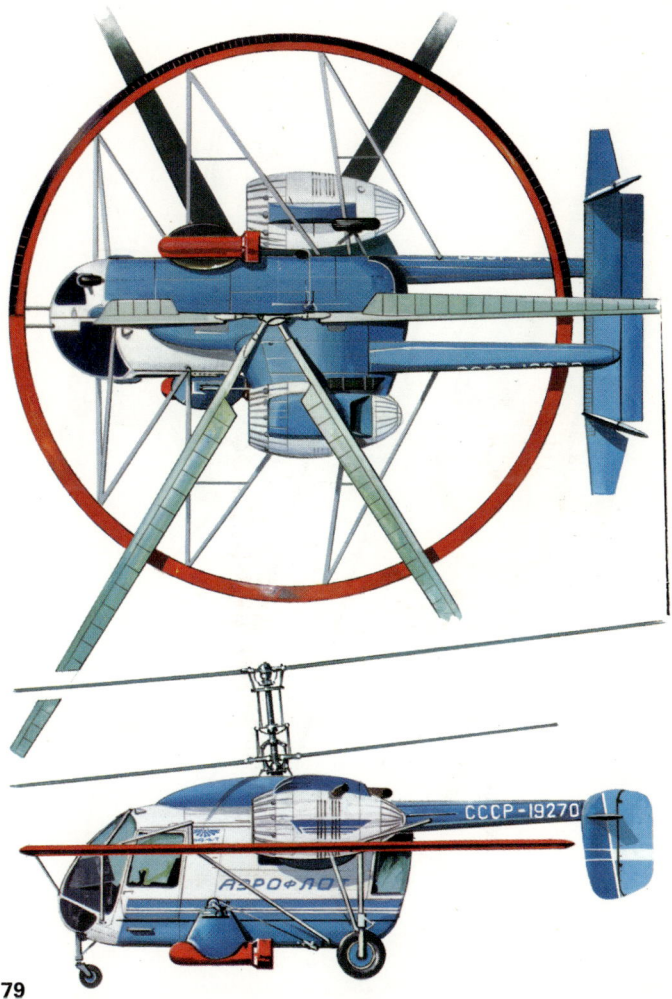

79

Kamov Ka-26, geological survey version, *ca* 1970. *Engines:* Two 325 h.p. Vedeneev M-14V-26 nine-cylinder radials. *Rotor diameter (each):* 42 ft. 7¾ in. (13·00 m.). *Fuselage length:* 25 ft. 5½ in. (7·75 m.). *Height:* 13 ft. 3½ in. (4·05 m.). *Maximum take-off weight:* 7,165 lb. (3,250 kg.). *Maximum speed:* 106 m.p.h. (170 km./hr.) at sea level. *Service ceiling:* 9,845 ft. (3,000 m.). *Maximum range with auxiliary fuel tanks:* 745 miles (1,200 km.).

CIERVA CR.LTH-1 (U.K.)

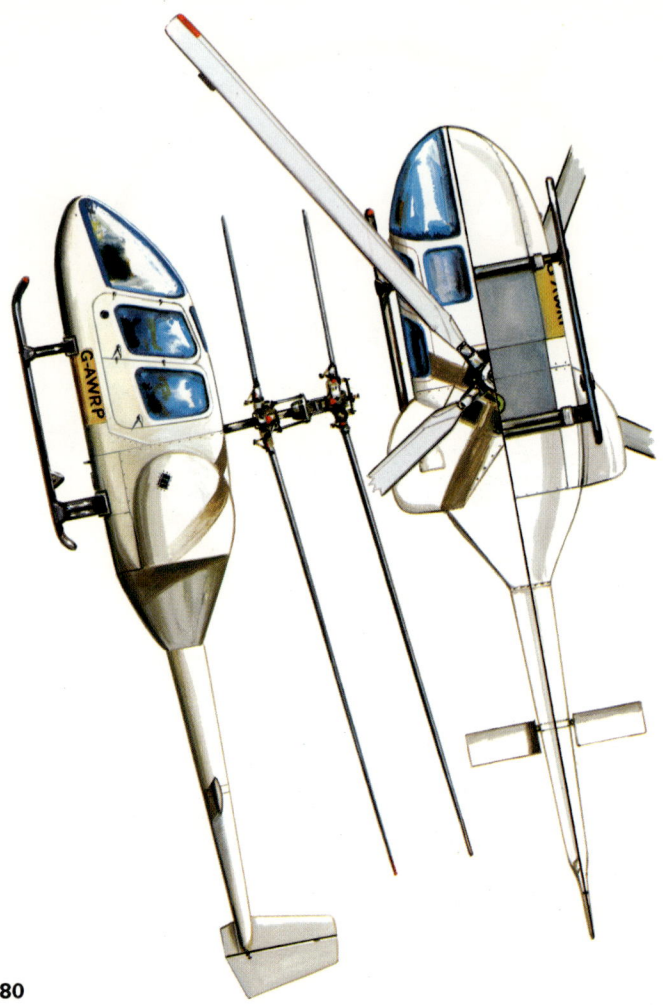

80

Cierva CR.LTH-1, second prototype, 1970. *Data apply to Twin 420 proposed production version. Engines:* Two 210 h.p. Continental TSIO-360-A six-cylinder horizontally-opposed type. *Rotor diameter (each):* 33 ft. 0 in. (10·06 m.). *Fuselage length:* 28 ft. 2 in. (8·58 m.). *Height:* 10 ft. 3½ in. (3·14 m.). *Maximum take-off weight:* 3,450 lb. (1,565 kg.). *Maximum speed:* 138 m.p.h. (222 km/hr.). *Service ceiling:* over 20,000 ft. (6,100 m.). *Maximum range:* 450 miles (724 km.).

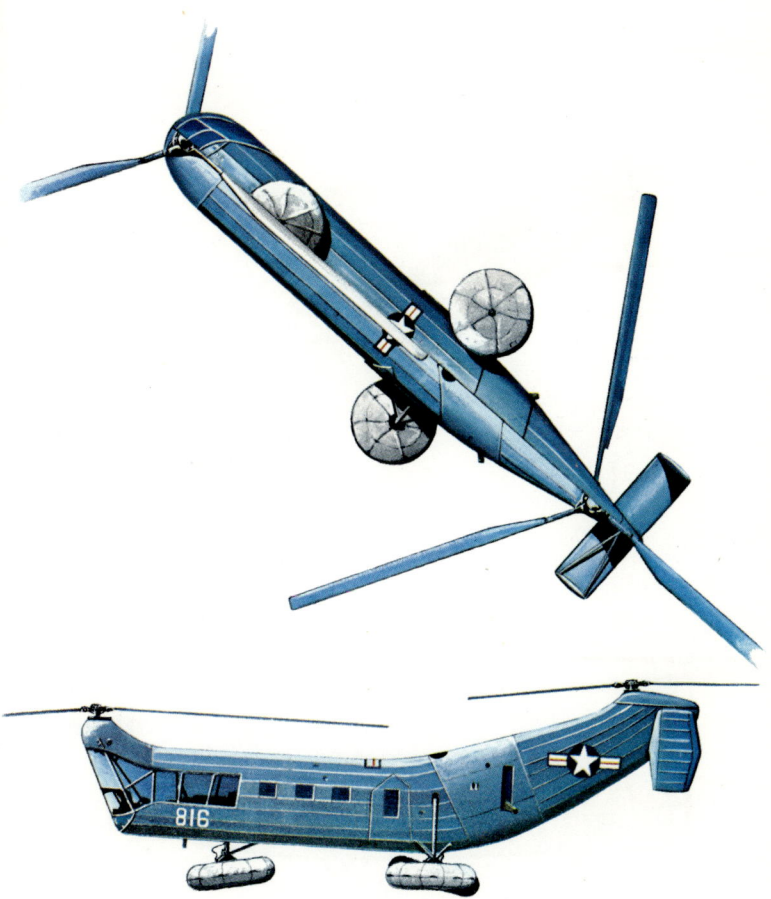

81

Piasecki HRP-1 Rescuer of the U.S. Navy, *ca.* 1949. *Engine:* One 600 h.p. Pratt & Whitney R-1340-AN-1 Wasp nine-cylinder radial. *Rotor diameter (each):* 41 ft. 0 in. (12·50 m.). *Fuselage length:* 48 ft. 0 in. (14·63 m.). *Height:* 12 ft. 6 in. (3·81 m.). *Maximum take-off weight:* 6,900 lb. (3,130 kg.). *Maximum speed:* 99 m.p.h. (159 km./hr.). at 2,500 ft. (762 m.). *Service ceiling:* 10,400 ft. (3,170 m.). *Normal range:* 265 miles (426 km.).

BELL HSL-1 (U.S.A.)

82

Bell HSL-1 of the U.S. Navy, 1957. *Engine:* One 2,400 h.p. Pratt & Whitney R-2800-
50 Double Wasp eighteen-cylinder radial. *Rotor diameter (each):* 51 ft. 6 in.
(15·70 m.). *Fuselage length:* 39 ft. 2¾ in. (11·96 m.). *Height:* 14 ft. 6 in. (4·42 m.).
Maximum take-off weight: 26,500 lb. (12,020 kg.). *Maximum speed:* 138 m.p.h.
(222 km./hr.) at sea level. *Range:* 350 miles (563 km.).

83

Vertol HUP-2 Retriever of the U.S. Navy, *ca.* 1956. *Engine:* One 550 h.p. Continental R-975-46 nine-cylinder radial. *Rotor diameter (each):* 35 ft. 0 in. (10·67 m.). *Fuselage length:* 32 ft. 0 in. (9·75 m.). *Height:* 13 ft. 2 in. (4.01 m.). *Normal take-off weight:* 5,750 lb. (2,608 kg.). *Maximum speed:* 108 m.p.h. (174 km./hr.) at sea level. *Hovering ceiling in ground effect:* 7,000 ft. (2,134 m.). *Typical range:* 340 miles (547 km.).

BELVEDERE (U.K.)

84

Westland (Bristol) Belvedere HC Mk. 1 of No. 66 Squadron R.A.F., 1963. *Engines:* Two 1,650 s.h.p. Napier Gazelle Mk. 101 turboshafts. *Rotor diameter (each):* 48 ft. 11 in. (14·91 m.). *Fuselage length:* 54 ft. 4 in. (16·56 m.). *Height:* 17 ft. 3 in. (5·26 m.). *Maximum take-off weight:* 19,000 lb. (8,618 kg.). *Maximum cruising speed:* 138 m.p.h. (222 km./hr.) at sea level. *Service ceiling:* 17,300 ft. (5,270 m.). *Range with maximum payload of 6,000 lb. (2,722 kg.):* 75 miles (121 km.).

Yak-24 (U.S.S.R.)

85

Yakovlev Yak 24U of the Soviet Air Force, *ca* 1958. *Engines:* Two 1,700 h.p.
Shvetsov ASh-82V fourteen-cylinder radials. *Rotor diameter (each):* 68 ft. 10¾ in.
(21·00 m.). *Fuselage length:* 69 ft. 10½ in. (21·30 m.). *Height:* 21 ft. 4 in. (6·50 m.).
Maximum take-off weight: 32,276 lb. (14,640 kg.). *Maximum speed:* 158 m.p.h.
(254 km./hr.) at sea level. *Service ceiling:* 18,045 ft. (5,500 m.). *Range:* 298 miles
(480 km.).

Mi-12 (U.S.S.R.)

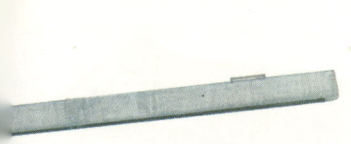

86

Mil Mi-12 (V-12) displayed at Le Bourget, May/June 1971. *Engines:* Four 6,500 s.h.p. Soloviev D-25VF turboshafts. *Rotor diameter (each):* 114 ft. 10 in. (35·00 m.). *Fuselage length:* 121 ft. 4½ in. (37·00 m.). *Height overall:* 41 ft. 0 in. (12·50 m.). *Maximum take-off weight:* 231,500 lb. (105,000 kg.). *Maximum speed:* 161 m.p.h. (260 km/hr.). *Service ceiling:* 11,500 ft. (3,500 m.). *Range with payload of 78,000 lb. (35,400 kg.):* 310 miles (500 km.).

VERTOL 43 and 44 (U.S.A.)

87
Vertol Model 43 (CH-21C) of the Federal German *Heeresflieger*, 1966. *Engine:*
One 1,425 h.p. Wright R-1820-103 Cyclone nine-cylinder radial. *Rotor diameter
(each):* 44 ft. 0 in. (13·41 m.). *Fuselage length:* 52 ft. 6 in. (16·00 m.). *Height:*
15 ft. 5 in. (4·70 m.). *Maximum take-off weight:* 14,704 lb. (6,669 kg.). *Maximum
speed:* 125 m.p.h. (202 km./hr.) at sea level. *Service ceiling:* 7,750 ft. (2,362 m.).
Normal range: 403 miles (649 km.).

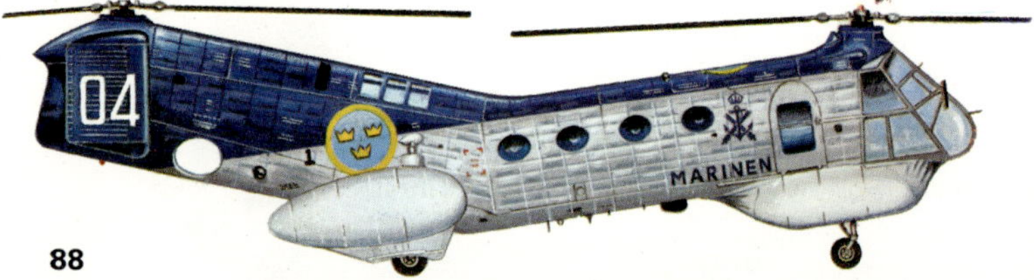

88
Boeing-Vertol Model 44A (HKP 1) of the *Kungl. Svenska Marinen*, 1962. *Engine:*
One 1,425 h.p. Wright 977C9HD1 Cyclone nine-cylinder radial. *Dimensions:* as for
Model 43. *Maximum take-off weight:* 14,350 lb. (6,509 kg.). *Maximum speed:*
127 m.p.h. (204 km./hr.) at sea level. *Service ceiling:* 8,900 ft. (2,713 m.). *Normal
range:* 288 miles (463 km.).

89

Kawasaki (Boeing-Vertol) KV-107/II-5 of the Japan Air Self-Defence Force, *ca* 1968-69. *Engines:* Two 1,250 s.h.p. General Electric CT58-110-1 turboshafts. *Rotor diameter (each):* 50 ft. 0 in. (15·24 m.). *Fuselage length:* 44 ft. 7 in. (13·59 m.). *Height:* 16 ft. 8½ in. (5·09 m.). *Maximum take-off weight:* 19,000 lb. (8,618 kg.). *Maximum cruising speed:* 157 m.p.h. (253 km/hr.) at sea level. *Service ceiling:* 13,000 ft. (3,960 m.). *Range with maximum fuel:* 745 miles (1,200 km.).

BOEING-VERTOL 107-II (U.S.A.)

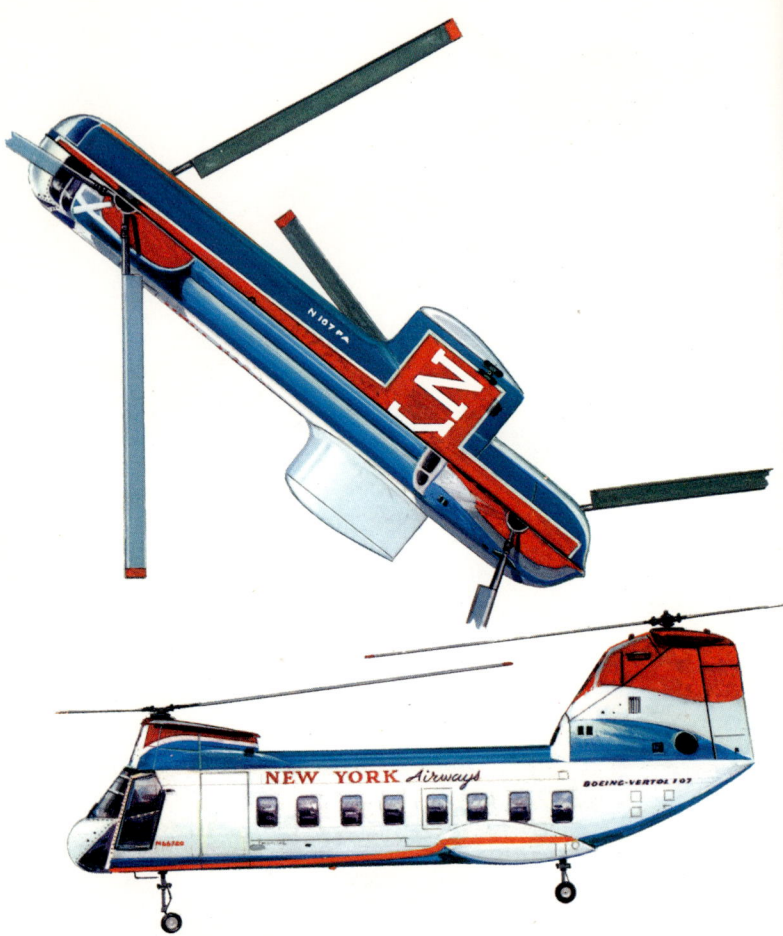

90

Boeing-Vertol 107-II of New York Airways Inc., 1962. *Engines:* Two 1,250 s.h.p. General Electric CT58-110-1 turboshafts. *Rotor diameter (each):* 50 ft. 0 in. (15·24 m.). *Fuselage length:* 44 ft. 7 in. (13·59 m.). *Height:* 16 ft. 8½ in. (5·09 m.). *Maximum take-off weight:* 19,000 lb. (8,618 kg.). *Maximum cruising speed:* 157 m.p.h. (253 km./hr.) at sea level. *Service ceiling:* 13,000 ft. (3,960 m.). *Range with payload of 6,600 lb (2,994 kg.):* 109 miles (175 km.).

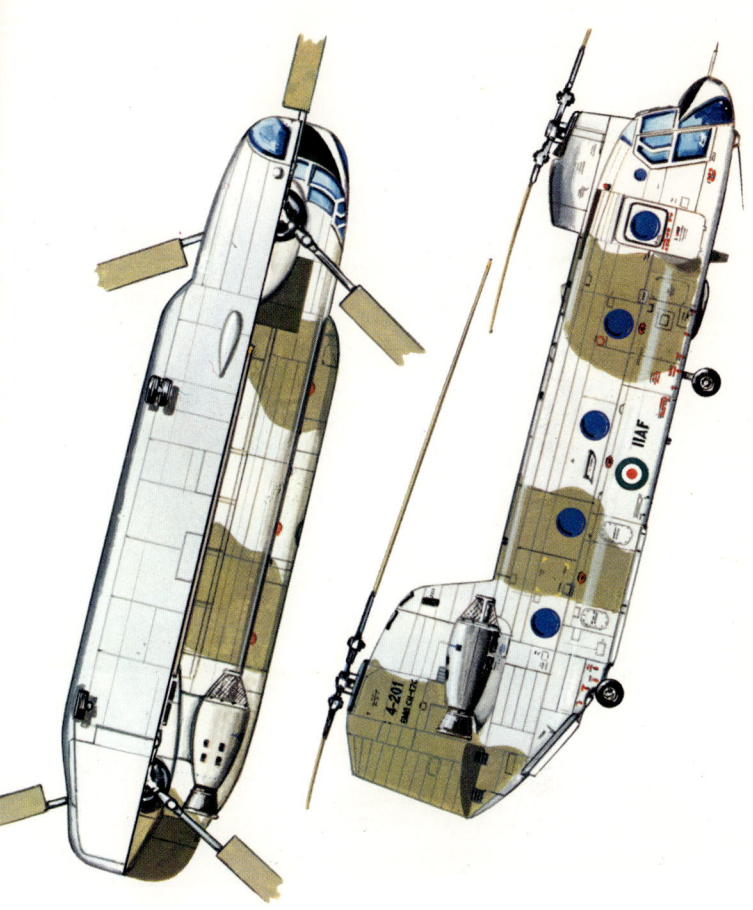

91

Meridionali-assembled Boeing-Vertol CH-47C Chinook of the Imperial Iranian Air Force, 1971. *Engines:* Two 3,750 s.h.p. Lycoming T55-L-11 turboshafts. *Rotor diameter (each):* 60 ft. 0 in. (18·29 m.). *Fuselage length:* 51 ft. 0 in. (15·54 m.). *Height:* 18 ft. 7 in. (5·67 m.). *Maximum take-off weight:* 46,000 lb. (20,865 kg.). *Maximum speed:* 190 m.p.h. (306 km./hr.) at sea level. *Service ceiling:* 15,000 ft. (4,570 m.). *Typical range:* 230 miles (370 km.). *(Performance data are for CH-47C at 33,000 lb. (14,970 kg.) take-off weight.)*

ROTODYNE (U.K.)

92

Westland (Fairey) Rotodyne prototype in manufacturer's demonstration finish,
April 1958. *Engines:* Two 3,000 e.h.p. (2,800 s.h.p.) Napier N.El.3 turboprops. *Rotor
diameter:* 90 ft. 0 in. (27·43 m.). *Wing span:* 46 ft. 6 in. (14·17 m.). *Fuselage length:*
58 ft. 8 in. (17·88 m.). *Height:* 22 ft. 2 in. (6·76 m.). *Maximum take-off weight:*
38,000 lb. (17,237 kg.). *Maximum cruising speed:* 185 m.p.h. (298 km./hr.) at
5,000 ft. (1,524 m.). *Maximum range:* 450 miles (724 km.).

93

Kamov Ka-22 *Vintokryl* displayed in Aviation Day parade, Moscow, July 1961. *Engines:* Two 5,500 s.h.p. Soloviev D-25V (TV-2) turboshafts. *Rotor diameter (each):* 65 ft. 7⅞ in. (20·00 m.). *Wing span:* 67 ft. 3⅛ in. (20·50 m.). *Fuselage length:* 73 ft. 9¾ in. (22·50 m.). *Height:* 27 ft. 0¾ in. (8·25 m.). *Maximum take-off weight:* 74,296 lb. (33,700 kg.). *Maximum speed:* 234 m.p.h. (377 km./hr.) at sea level.

PATHFINDER II (U.S.A.)

94

Piasecki 16H-1A Pathfinder II, 1965. *Engine:* One 1,250 s.h.p. General Electric T58-GE-5 turboshaft. *Rotor diameter:* 44 ft. 0 in. (13·41 m.). *Wing span:* approx. 24 ft. 0 in. (7·32 m.). *Fuselage length:* 37 ft. 3 in. (11·35 m.). *Height:* 11 ft. 4 in. (3·45 m.). *Maximum vertical take-off weight:* 8,150 lb. (3,697 kg.). *Maximum speed:* 230 m.p.h. (370 km/hr.). *Service ceiling:* 18,700 ft. (5,700 m.). *Range with maximum payload:* 450 miles (725 km.).

1 Breguet-Richet helicopters

When it rose vertically from the ground with its pilot in the late summer of 1907, the Gyroplane No 1 built by Louis and Jacques Breguet in association with Professor Charles Richet had to be steadied by a man stationed at the extremity of each of the four arms supporting the rotors. It cannot, therefore, take the credit for being the first helicopter to make a free flight, even though the ground helpers contributed nothing towards the lifting power of the rotors; but it was the first machine to raise itself, with a pilot, vertically off the ground by means of a rotating-wing system of lift. Basically, the Breguet machine consisted of a rectangular central chassis of steel tubing supporting the powerplant and the pilot; from each corner of this chassis there radiated an arm, also of steel tube construction, at the extremity of which was mounted a fabric-covered 4-blade biplane rotor, making a total of 32 small lifting surfaces. One pair of diagonally opposed rotors rotated in a clockwise direction, the other pair moving anti-clockwise. The pilot, M Volumard, was reputedly chosen at least partly because of his small stature – he weighed only 150 lb (68 kg). Authorities differ over the date of the Breguet machine's first flight at Douai, 24 August and 19 September 1907 being quoted with equal assurance, though the latter date is the one more generally accepted; on this occasion the aircraft rose to about 0·60 m (2 ft). Take-off to some 1·50 m (5 ft) was achieved during a test on 29 September, and similar heights were reached in several subsequent tests, but the Breguet-Richet aircraft was neither controllable nor steerable in a horizontal plane.

In 1908 the Breguet-Richet collaboration produced a No 2 Gyroplane, powered by a 55 hp Renault engine and having two forward-tilting 2-blade rotors with a diameter of 7·85 m (25 ft 9 in) and, in addition, fixed wings giving an extra 50 sq m (538 sq ft) of lifting surface. This machine made a number of successful flights in the summer of 1908, but was severely damaged in a 'heavy' landing on 19 September. In rebuilt form as the No 2bis it was displayed statically at Paris in December 1908 and made one test flight in the following April, but a month later the Breguet premises were wrecked by a hurricane. This, and the shortage of contemporary engines with an adequate power/weight ratio, caused Breguet to abandon rotary-winged development until the appearance of the Breguet-Dorand design in the 1930s.

2 Cornu helicopter

The first aeroplane to take off vertically with its pilot and make a free flight entirely without assistance from or connection with the ground was the 'flying bicycle' designed and built by Paul Cornu in 1907. It achieved this feat at Coquainvilliers, near Lisieux, on 13 November 1907, though the distinction is a slightly academic one since the aircraft remained in the air for only some 20 sec at an 'altitude' of about

0·30 m (1 ft). The chassis was in the form of an open 'Vee' supporting the engine, fuel tanks and pilot's seat in the centre and resting on a four-wheeled landing gear. The rotors were paddle-shaped and fabric-covered, mounted on large horizontal, bicycle-type wheels situated one at each end of the machine and turned by a belt drive from the engine. The design followed that of a small scale model made by Cornu a year or so previously with 2·25 m (7 ft 4⅝ in) rotors, a 2 hp Buchet engine and a weight of 13 kg (28·66 lb). The full-scale machine made its first flight – unmanned, with a 50 kg (110 lb) bag of soot occupying the pilot's seat – on 27 September 1907. It made its second manned ascent with Cornu's brother hanging on to the framework, increasing the total weight to 328 kg (623 lb), and take-offs to about 2 m (6½ ft) were made later carrying the pilot only. However, the helicopter's transmission system was suspect, its framework too flimsy, and – despite the movable fore and aft vanes – its controllability was largely ineffectual; and these factors, combined with a lack of funds, caused Cornu to forsake the further development of his historic but impractical design.

3 Ellehammer helicopters

Jacob Christian Ellehammer must surely rank among the most versatile of aviation's early pioneers. First apprenticed as a watchmaker, he then qualified as an electrical engineer; he made one of the earliest motor-cycles built in Denmark, and also designed his own internal combustion engines. His 3-cylinder piston engine of 1903 was perhaps the world's first radial engine, and his experiments in aviation, started two years later, embraced monoplanes, biplanes, triplanes, flying-boats and helicopters.

Ellehammer's first studies of rotary-winged flight began in 1910, and various experiments were carried out in 1911 with a scale model helicopter. The full-sized machine that he built in the following year would today be defined as a compound helicopter, for its 6 hp engine (also designed by Ellehammer) drove both the rotor system and a conventional propeller. The lifting rotors were of an ingenious pattern, consisting of two contra-rotating rings, each of 5·97 m (19 ft 7 in) diameter, the lower one being covered with fabric to increase the lift. At regular intervals round the perimeter of the wings were six vanes, each about 1·50 m (4 ft 11 in) long and 0·66 m (2 ft 2 in) wide and pivoting about its horizontal axis. The rotor system was driven via a hydraulic clutch and gearbox, all designed by Ellehammer, and the rotor vanes' angle could be altered in flight by the pilot – an early example of cyclic pitch control. After several successful indoor take-off tests, during which the machine was probably tethered, Ellehammer's machine made a free vertical take-off later in 1912, in front of witnesses who included HRH Prince Axel. Tests with the 1912 helicopter continued until late in September 1916, when it overturned after a take-off and the machine was wrecked when the rotors spun into the ground.

Ellehammer then put aside his helicopter experiments until about 1930, when he began to evolve some new projects. One of these was, in effect, a parasol monoplane in whose wings was a huge circular cut-out with two contra-rotating rotors turning inside it. Even more novel was a proposal in the mid-1930s for a helicopter driven by compressed air. As with the previous project, only a working model was built, powered by a vacuum cleaner motor. In the full-sized aircraft Ellehammer proposed to have a radial engine driving a powerful air compressor. A substantial pylon over the fuselage was topped by a metal disc, made to rotate by the reaction from expelling compressed air through slots in its underside. The centrifugal force of the rotating disc was sufficient to unsheath four spring-loaded rotor blades; when take-off had been accomplished, these were retracted back into the disc and the compressed air stream diverted to an efflux at the rear of the aircraft to give it forward movement.

4 Oehmichen helicopters

Etienne Oehmichen, a young engineer with the Peugeot motor car company, began to experiment with rotating-wing designs in 1920, and in all designed and built six different vertical take-off machines. When the first of these failed to develop enough lift from its twin rotors and 25 hp engine to rise off the ground, he added a hydrogen-filled balloon on top of it to give it added stability and lift. The most noteworthy – and most striking – of his aircraft was the helicopter No 2, which had no fewer than 4 rotors and 8 propellers, all driven by a single 120 hp Le Rhône rotary engine when it flew for the first time on 11 November 1922. A 180 hp Gnome engine was substituted later. The Oehmichen No 2 was basically a steel-tube framework of cruciform layout, with 2-blade paddle-shaped rotors at the extremities of the four arms. The angle of these blades could be varied by warping. Five of the propellers, turning in a horizontal plane, served to stabilise the machine laterally; another propeller mounted at the nose was for steering the helicopter; and the remaining pair acted as pusher propellers for forward propulsion. The opposing pairs of rotors were of slightly different diameters. The Oehmichen No 2 exhibited, for its time, a considerable degree of stability and controllability, and in all made more than a thousand test flights during the middle 1920s. By 1923 it was able to remain airborne for several minutes at a time, and on 14 April 1924 it established the first-ever FAI distance record for helicopters of 1,181 ft (360 m). Three days later it increased this to 1,722 ft (525 m) and on 4 May was airborne for 14 min, flying more than a mile and completing in the process the first 1 km closed-circuit flight by a helicopter in 7 min 40 sec. Oehmichen was, however, dissatisfied with the modest heights to which No 2 was able to fly, and from the third machine onward he adopted a single main rotor layout, accompanied by two smaller anti-torque rotors. His last design, in 1938, reverted to the balloon-assisted principle of his first aircraft.

5 Pescara helicopters

It is unfortunate that more complete records have evidently not survived of the later Pescara helicopters, for despite their apparent clumsiness they represented for their time an important step forward in helicopter design technology that deserves recognition. The Spanish Marquis Raul Pateras Pescara built his first helicopter in Barcelona in 1919–20. It was a clumsy machine, weighing some 600 kg (1,323 lb) without fuel or pilot and powered by a 45 hp Hispano engine. Each of the 2 co-axial rotors had a diameter of 6·40 m (21 ft 0 in) and was made up of 6 biplane pairs of blades giving a total of 24 lifting surfaces, but the little Hispano was not powerful enough to raise the machine off the ground. A modified form of this aircraft, with a 170 hp Le Rhône rotary engine, did just get off the ground in May 1921, but it was far from being a stable or satisfactory design. In 1922 Pescara moved to France, where the No 2 did succeed in rising some 1·5 m (5 ft) during tests carried out for the Service Technique de l'Aéronautique.

Pescara's most successful helicopter was the No 3, which was built in 1923 and by January 1924 was capable of making flights of some 10 minutes' duration. The same co-axial rotor system was employed, larger twin rotors each with 4 pairs of blades turning around a 'totem pole' rotor mast. A 180 hp Hispano-Suiza engine, for which the Lamblin radiator was situated at the rear of the craft, provided the power. Although a heavy and cumbersome machine the Pescara No 3 was a simple design when compared with its closest contemporary, the Oehmichen No 2, and makes an interesting comparison with the Breguet-Dorand of some ten years later. On 18 April 1924 Pescara flew the No 3 at Issy-les-Moulineaux for a distance of 736 m (805 yds), handsomely beating the record set up by the Oehmichen only the day before.

The significance of this achievement lay in the fact that Pescara's machine, unlike the Oehmichen or any other rotorcraft up to that time, did not rely on conventional propellers rotating in the vertical plane to give the aircraft forward motion. Instead, the pitch of the 16 lifting surfaces could be altered in flight by warping them, and the rotor head could be tilted to give the blades a degree of forward thrust. The speeds thus achieved were extremely modest, but the Pescara No 3 exhibited the first convincing demonstration of the principles of cyclic and collective pitch control. Autorotation of the rotors was also provided for in the event of engine failure.

Reference is made in some quarters to the Pescara No 3F, which was possibly a modification of the No 3 and not a new machine. This appeared in the early part of 1925 and had a 250 hp engine, with a cut-down propeller fulfilling a cooling function only. It offered no great improvement over the No 3, and later that year Pescara returned to Spain and entered the motor car industry. He seems to have been discouraged from further serious helicopter development by the emergent success of Cierva with the Autogiro, though he was associated with the little French-designed Pouit S-4 later in the 1920s.

6 Cierva C.1 to C.40

Juan de la Cierva, the Spanish engineer who has justifiably been called 'one of the greatest original thinkers aviation has ever known', and who produced or influenced the design of almost every successful Autogiro to appear between World Wars 1 and 2, became interested in rotary-winged flight when he first studied it as a potential means of curing stalling problems in fixed-wing aircraft. His first three Autogiros, built in 1920–22, had non-flexible rotor blades and were all unsuccessful, but in 1922 he built a scale model with articulated hinges that allowed the blades to flap. Each retreating blade could therefore flex downward as the advancing one's air-speed lifted it up, so that the lift forces were in balance and prevented the aircraft's tendency to become unstable and roll over while in flight. Cierva applied this principle to his C.4 design, which duly made a successful first flight near Madrid on 9 January 1923 and by the end of

that month had covered a 4 km (2½ mile) closed circuit in 4 min at an average height of about 30 m (100 ft). A single-seater, the C.4 was based on a Hanriot fuselage and had a 110 hp Le Rhône 9Ja rotary engine and a 4-blade rotor. The C.5, flown in July 1923, was similar except for a 3-blade rotor, while the C.6A returned to a 4-blade rotor and utilised the fuselage of an Avro 504N training biplane. The C.6A first flew in May 1924, and just over a year later Cierva brought it to Britain, demonstrating it at the Royal Aircraft Establishment in October 1925. As a result, Avro was asked to build two similar aircraft, the single-seat C.6C (J8068) and the 2-seat C.6D (G-EBTW), both powered by 130 hp Clerget rotaries. The latter machine flew for the first time on 29 July 1926, later being built as the C.8R with a larger rotor. The C.8V was similar to this except for its Viper in-line engine, and was followed by three C.8L's with Lynx radials and one with a 225 hp Wright Whirlwind. The second (or Mk II) C.8L illustrated made the historic first-ever crossing of the English Channel by a rotary-winged aircraft on 18 September 1928 when Cierva, with a French journalist as passenger, flew it from Croydon to Le Bourget.

Meanwhile, in 1926 Cierva had formed his own company in Britain, and in the ensuing years licences were granted to manufacturers in Britain, France, Germany, Japan and the USA to build Autogiros of the Cierva type. In most cases these used the Cierva rotor system allied to a convenient fuselage from an existing fixed-wing type – sometimes with small stub wings added – but several completely fresh designs also appeared. Thus the Avro-built C.6 and C.8 were based on the Avro 504, and the C.9, the floatplane C.12 and the C.17 on the Avian; and Comper's C.25 was based on the Swift. Generally similar developments in the United States included a range of Autogiros built by Pitcairn, the Kellett KD-1 and the pusher-engined Buhl. On all Cierva types up to and including the C.18 the rotor had to be started manually by pulling on a rope wound round the shaft. The C.19 was the first to introduce automatic starting and was one of the most successful designs, being built by Focke in Germany as well as by Avro. An attractive variant was the de Havilland-built C.24 (later remodelled as the C.26) first flown in September 1931. Whereas previous designs had had open cockpits, the C.24 was a handsome cabin 2-seater in which Cierva made an extensive European demonstration tour in May/June 1932. The CL.10 and CL.20 were other cabin variants designed by Le Père and built respectively by Lioré et Olivier in France and Westland in the United Kingdom. Westland also produced a prototype of the 5-seat C.29, but this aircraft was destroyed by ground resonance before it had flown.

The C.30 (described separately) marked the next major advance in the Cierva line, by having direct rotor control by means of a column suspended from the head of the pylon which acted directly on the rotor head to tilt it to produce the desired manoeuvre. In 1933 Cierva also successfully evolved the principle of 'jump starting' an Autogiro – which until then had required a short take-off and landing run – and the first new design to embody this feature was the C.40, produced in 1937 by the British Aircraft Manufacturing Co with a 175 hp Salmson engine and a new, vibrationless rotor head partially enclosing the 2-seat cockpit.

The death of Cierva in an airliner crash in December 1936, and the successful evolution soon afterwards of practical helicopters, virtually ended further development of the Autogiro as a type, although this form of rotorcraft has enjoyed something of a renaissance in recent years.

7 Cierva C.30A

The Cierva C.30A marked a major step forward in rotorcraft development, being the first production Autogiro in which the engine was geared directly to drive the rotor blades for take-off. The degree of direct control was increased still further by having the control column, which acted directly on the rotor, suspended from the pylon so that the rotor head could be tilted in any direction to produce the manoeuvre desired. The new-style control system was first installed in G-ABXP, a Cierva C.19 designated Mk V with a 100 hp Genet Major I engine. This was basically a C.19 Mk IV modified to have a clutch and transmission shaft, a tilting rotor head and (later) a small, fixed tailplane.

The prototype C.30 (G-ACFI) differed chiefly in having a tripod rotor pylon and dihedral on the tailplane tips; the fuselage was modified by Airwork from a standard C.19, and assembly was undertaken by National Flying Services at Hanworth, where G-ACFI made its maiden flight early in April 1933. Take-off run of the C.30 was about 30 yards (27·43 m), while the landing was achieved in about 3 yards (2·74 m) with the rotor blades autorotating. Another 1933 prototype was G-ACKA, the first C.30P, with 140 hp Genet Major IA, folding rotor blades and other improvements. First customer for the production C.30A was the Royal Air Force, for whom the type was built by Avro and given the name Rota. One twin-float Sea Rota (K4296) and ten standard Rotas with wheeled undercarriages were completed to Specification 16/35, and were delivered to the School of Army Co-operation from December 1934. One other military C.30A was K4775, a Civet Major-engined machine sent to the Royal Aircraft Establishment in 1935 for blade-flexing tests. Avro production of C.30 types was in the region of seventy aircraft, three of which were C.30P's. Thirty-seven C.30A's appeared on the pre-war British civil register, and others were completed for customers in Europe, India, China, Australia and South Africa. In Britain the C.30A, like the C.19 before it, was used for traffic reporting duties at major sporting and similar events, and one aircraft (G-ACUT) was used for filming the 1936 FA Cup Final.

During 1933 the C.30 prototype, G-ACFI, was converted for jump-start trials with a modified rotor head, and in 1936 a perfected form of this was fitted to G-ACWF when it made the first genuine vertical take-off by an Autogiro, by keeping the engine and rotor system engaged throughout the take-off sequence. This machine was, in effect, the prototype for the C.40, five of which were ordered for the RAF as the Rota II to Specification 2/36. These were built by the British Aircraft Manufacturing Co, having side-by-side seats, wooden semi-monocoque fuselages and 175 hp Salmson 9NG engines. Two of the original five Rota II's were diverted to civilian customers, replacements being built in 1938–39. The RAF C.40's served with No 1448 Flight (later 529 Squadron). On the outbreak of World War 2 over a dozen civil C.30A's were impressed for military service; these and the surviving Rota I's were allocated singly to RAF radar stations in the United Kingdom for calibration duties.

8, 9 & 10 TsAGI rotorcraft

Some of the earliest notions of rotating-wing flight originated in Russia, the earliest known instance being a demonstration in 1754 by the scientist Mikhail Lomonosov of a string-suspended, spring-driven model screw. At the beginning of the 20th century, apart from Igor Sikorsky, several Russian pioneers built or tested rotorcraft designs, though none with significant results. K. A. Antonov's 'Helikoplan', an underpowered machine completed in 1910, had two co-axial multiblade rotors, but more prophetic were the two rotorcraft designed in 1911 by Boris N. Yuriev, which adopted the now-classic 'pennyfarthing' arrangement of a single main rotor and small anti-torque tail rotor which was eventually adopted by Sikorsky in his much later VS-300 (which see). Yuriev,

department was known at first as the Experimental Aerodynamic Department, and later as the Special Design Section. It was Skrzhinskii, aided by Nikolai Kamov, who designed the first successful Soviet rotorcraft, both their names being incorporated in its designation KaSkr-I. Using the fuselage of a U-1 (Soviet-built Avro 504K), with wider-track main landing gear and 26 ft 3 in (8·00 m) span monoplane wings, the KaSkr-I Autogiro was powered by a 110 hp Le Rhône

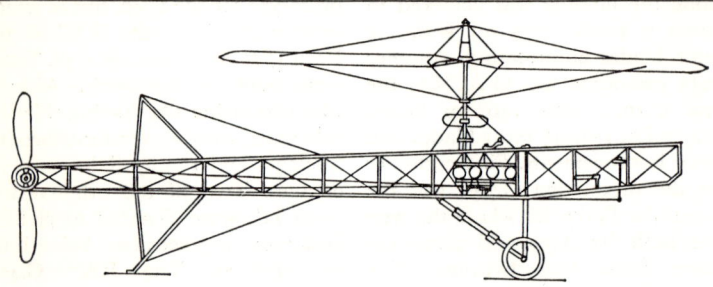

Side view drawing (*via Jean Alexander*) of the second helicopter designed by Yuriev in 1911. Intended powerplant was a 70 hp Gnome rotary engine, main rotor diameter was 29 ft 6¼ in (9·00 m), and design gross weight 860 lb (390 kg). A developed version, built in 1912, had a 27/30 hp Anzani engine, 26 ft 3 in (8·00 m) main rotor and gross weight of 447·5 lb (203 kg). It received a Gold Medal design award, but unfortunately the rotor shaft broke during ground tests and the aircraft never flew.

indeed, may well be regarded as the 'father' of modern Soviet rotorcraft development, and after the TsAGI (Central Aero and Hydrodynamic Institute) set up a rotorcraft research department in 1925 its leading designers included Yuriev, I. P. Bratukhin (from 1926), V. A. Kuznetsov (from 1928 or 1929) and N. K. Skrzhinskii (from 1931). The

rotary engine and had a gross weight of 2,094 lb (950 kg). It was fitted with a 4-blade rotor of 39 ft 4½ in (12·00 m) diameter, and seated a pilot and passenger in tandem open cockpits. The KaSkr-I was underpowered, but made a number of flights in 1929–30 before being refitted with a 230 hp Gnome-Rhône Titan five-cylinder radial engine and redesignated KaSkr-II. In this form it had a maximum speed of 68·4 mph (110 km/hr) at a gross weight of 2,425 lb (1,100 kg); it made 90 flights, the longest lasting for 28 minutes.

Meanwhile, in 1928 Yuriev had begun design of the first Soviet helicopter, the TsAGI 1-EA. A single-seater, the 1-EA was powered by two 120 hp M-2 engines and had an openwork steel-tube fuselage, tapered at each end. The powerplant, located behind the pilot, drove a 36 ft 1 in (11·00 m) diameter 4-blade main rotor and two pairs of 2-blade contra-rotating steering rotors, one each side of the frame at the front and another pair at the rear. A ground test rig of the rotor system, built in 1928, provided some forecast of the 1-EA's handling qualities, and tethered flight trials of the helicopter began in August 1930. Design work, after Yuriev left the TsAGI earlier that year, was completed by A. M. Isakson, and the test flying was carried out by A. M. Cheremukhin. This lasted for almost 3 years, and proved the 1-EA to have an encouragingly good performance and endurance, though its controllability was poor. It weighed 2,524 lb (1,145 kg) for take-off, and flew at speeds of about 12·4 to 18·6 mph (20 to 30 km/hr); its most notable performance was to reach a record height of 1,985 ft (605 m) on 14 August 1932 – considerably better than the existing figure of 59 ft (18 m) reached by the little Italian d'Ascanio helicopter 2 years earlier. The 1-EA crashed in June 1933, but was rebuilt and used in 1933–34 for pilot training and other work. A second 1-EA had been started; this was completed in slightly-modified form as the 3-EA and subjected to ground tests and some tethered flights. In an attempt to improve upon the controllability of the helicopter Ivan P. Bratukhin, who had been appointed to head the enquiry into the crash of the original 1-EA, designed a new main rotor system. This was fitted to the 3-EA, which was then redesignated 5-EA. The new main rotor was enlarged to 39 ft 4½ in (12·00 m) diameter, and consisted of 3 main lifting blades and 3 shorter intermediate blades, the latter being control blades with adjustable cyclic pitch. The 5-EA continued to fly for some 3 years, and its controllability was considerably better than that of its predecessors, but the gross weight had risen to 2,667·5 lb (1,210 kg) and overall performance was inferior. Bratukhin was also responsible for the TsAGI's only other pre-war helicopter, the 11-EA. This was altogether a larger aircraft, being a 2-seat winged helicopter with a 630 hp Curtiss V-1570 Conqueror engine, a 50 ft 6¼ in (15·40 m) main rotor of similar pattern to that of the 5-EA, and a gross weight of 5,732 lb (2,600 kg). A single 3-blade anti-torque rotor was mounted near each wingtip. Design began in 1934; development, halted a year or two later, was completed in 1938, and tethered tests were then carried out. Later still, the new designation 11-EA-PV was allotted when all-metal rotor blades were fitted and the wings were replaced by steel-tube outrigger structures each bearing a pair of tandem-mounted anti-torque rotors at the tips. Loaded weight was thus reduced to 4,960 lb (2,250 kg), and speeds of 31–37 mph (50–60 km/hr) were obtained. The first free flights were made in October 1940 by the 11-EA-PV, and testing continued until the engine was no longer serviceable.

Throughout the 1930s, active development of Autogiros continued at the TsAGI, with particular note being paid to the work of Cierva; a Cierva C.30A was purchased in 1935. Following the 2-EA, Kuznetsov (with assistance from M. L. Mil) retained the same basic airframe, except for a modified tail unit, in his next design, the A-4, which was completed and first flown in 1932. With the more powerful M-26 engine, enclosed in a Townend cowling ring, the A-4 went into limited production – the first Soviet rotorcraft to do so – and its development was further continued in the A-6, A-8, A-13 and A-14. (The A-9 and A-10 were unbuilt projects.) The A-6 was essentially a smaller and more refined A-4, with a 100 hp M-11 uncowled five-cylinder radial engine and 36 ft 1 in (11·00 m) 3-blade rotor; it weighed 1,797 lb (815 kg) loaded and could reach 88 mph (142 km/hr). Provision was made for folding the wings and rotor, and construction of three aircraft was begun. Only one of these was completed as an A-6, and at one stage in its development was fitted with Vee tail surfaces. The other two A-6 airframes were completed as A-8's, retaining the same basic fuselage,

powerplant and rotor, but having shorter-span wings without dihedral tips, a modified main landing gear and small auxiliary fins on the tailplane. The A-8 was slightly heavier than the A-6, and flight testing began in 1935, but it did not go into production. The A-13 had modified wings with greater dihedral, a Townend ring for the M-11 engine, 'spatted' main wheels and other detail improvements. Gross weight was reduced to 1,759 lb (798 kg), and speed increased to 94 mph (151 km/hr), but again no production ensued. The A-14 was actually the second prototype A-8, from which the wings were removed in 1935; the tailplane instead had dihedral tips.

Kuznetsov's next Autogiro, the A-15, was also wingless, but much larger. Powered by a 700 hp M-25V radial engine, neatly enclosed in an NACA cowling, it had a 59 ft 0¾ in (18·00 m) 3-blade rotor, a gross weight of 5,644 lb (2,560 kg) and a top speed of 176 mph (283 km/hr). Designed for photographic and visual reconnaissance, it had an enclosed front cockpit and an open observer's position to the rear. Kuznetsov was also responsible for a 1940 design known as the AK, an Autogiro powered by a 220 hp MV-6 engine and having a 44 ft 3½ in (13·50 m) rotor. A prototype of the AK reached near-completion, but was abandoned after the USSR became involved in World War 2.

Nikolai Kamov, following his work on the KaSkr prototypes, was primarily responsible for the A-7 Autogiro, which appeared in 1934 and was displayed at Tushino in the following year. Powered by a Townend-ringed 480 hp M-22 radial engine, it had a 3-blade rotor of 49 ft 9¾ in (15·18 m) diameter, a gross weight of 4,533 lb (2,056 kg) and a maximum speed of 130 mph (210 km/hr). Other features included a faired tricycle landing gear. It seated 2 persons in open tandem cockpits, with provision for a machine-gun mounting in the rear one. About five were built for the Red Army, the production version being known as the A-7-bis and having small auxiliary fins and a re-designed rotor mast. They were used for night reconnaissance and leaflet dropping on the Smolensk front in 1941. Design of the TsAGI A-12, which was the Soviet Union's first wingless Autogiro, was shared between Skrzhinskii and M. L. Mil. A single-seater, it was also the first TsAGI rotorcraft to have an enclosed cockpit. Design work began in 1934, and the A-12 flew for the first time in 1936, achieving a speed of 152 mph (245 km/hr) in tests before crashing and killing its pilot in 1937.

11 **Kellett KD-1**

The products of the Kellett Autogiro Corporation, formed in 1929, showed strongly the influence of the early Cierva Autogiros, for which the American company held a manufacturing licence. Kellett's first Autogiro was the 2-seat K-2 of 1931, but its best-known design was the KD-1 which first appeared in late 1934. This was a direct control Autogiro (hence the D in the designation) and was also a 2-seater, the cockpits in this case being open and placed in tandem. The pylon for the 3-blade main rotor was situated immediately in front of the forward cockpit, and the blades could be folded back over the fuselage. Standard powerplant for the KD-1A production version was the 225 hp Jacobs L-4MA radial engine, the torque from which was corrected by giving the port and starboard tailplane halves opposing incidence.

On 19 May 1939 a single-seat converted KD-1A, still with an open cockpit, carried out a demonstration flight from the centre of Washington to the city's Hoover Airport with a cargo of mail. Two months later, on 6 July, a similar aircraft in Eastern Air Lines colours and with an enclosed cockpit (see illustration) commenced the first-ever scheduled air mail service by a rotary-winged aeroplane, between the Philadelphia Post Office and Camden Airport, New Jersey. This version of the Autogiro was known as the KD-1B, and it continued to operate the service for about 12 months. In 1935 the US Army Air Corps acquired one KD-1A for trials, giving it the designation YG-1. Subsequently it received one YG-1A, seven YG-1B's and seven XO-60's. One of the YG-1B's was converted to YG-1C and later to XR-2 with a 330 hp Jacobs L-6 engine, and another to XR-3 with a new rotor mounting after the XR-2 had suffered destruction due to ground resonance troubles. The XO-60 (later YO-60) was a further development in which the chief differences were a 300 hp Jacobs

R-915-3 engine, a bulged Perspex cabin enclosure and observation windows in the fuselage floor. Because of the advent of successful helicopter designs, notably those of Sikorsky, further military development of the YO-60 was discontinued after 1943. The Japanese government, after acquiring and testing a KD-1A in 1939, turned the aircraft over to the Kayaba Industrial Co, which subsequently built a version of the aircraft powered by a 240 hp Kobe-built version of the German Argus As 10C engine and known as the Ka-1; the first Ka-1 was flown on 26 May 1941 and eventually some two hundred and forty aircraft of this type were built. They were employed during World War 2 by the Imperial Japanese Army for 2-seat artillery observation and co-operation duties, and by the Navy for single-seat coastal or carrier-based anti-submarine patrol carrying two 60 kg (132 lb) bombs or depth charges. One Ka-1 was modified for trials with small auxiliary rockets at the tips of the rotor blades, and another was redesignated Ka-2 after refitting with a 240 hp Jacobs L-4MA-7 engine.

Some fifteen years after the end of World War 2 the KD-1A design was resurrected and offered as a production Autogiro, either in its original open-cockpit form or with a YO-60-type cabin hood and a fully-cowled Jacobs R-775-9 of 225 hp.

12 Breguet-Dorand Gyroplane Laboratoire

After the destruction of the Breguet-Richet No 2bis helicopter in 1909, Louis Breguet suspended his experiments into the problems connected with rotary-winged flight in order to concentrate on the development of fixed-wing aircraft. However, towards the end of the 1920s he returned to the study of helicopters and in 1929–30 took out patents for systems for stabilising aircraft of this type while in flight. In 1931 he formed the Syndicat d'Etudes du Gyroplane, with René Dorand (who had joined the Breguet company in 1924) as technical director, and began the design and construction of an experimental machine known as the Gyroplane Laboratoire. Intended originally to be powered by a 240 hp Breguet-Bugatti engine, it consisted basically of a steel-tube open framework supporting the engine, fuel tank, flight controls and pilot, with rear booms carrying the plywood-covered tail surfaces. An unusually wide track main undercarriage was mounted on outriggers from the central framework, with a small tailwheel and a nosewheel to prevent the machine tipping forward on landing. The transmission from the big radial engine drove a pair of co-axial, counter-rotating, 2-blade metal rotors whose blades had an aerofoil section and an unusually large diameter. One rotor shaft turned inside the other, each rotor thus cancelling out the torque created by the other. Novel features for the time were the use of a cyclic pitch control for lateral and longitudinal movement, and collective pitch for movement in the vertical plane.

The achievements of the Breguet-

Dorand aeroplane, eclipsed by the more widely publicised efforts of its near contemporary, the Focke-Wulf Fw 61, have been accorded less prominence than they deserve. The later Fw 61 was demonstrably the superior machine of the two, but the advance in helicopter technology brought by the French design is most apparent when compared with the best that had gone before it. It is believed that the Breguet-Dorand aircraft was completed by November 1933: it was then little more than three years since the small Italian d'Ascanio machine had set up FAI distance, height and endurance records of 1·078 km (3,538·7 ft), 18 m (59 ft), and 8 min 45·2 sec respectively. Within a year and a half of its first flight on 26 June 1935 the Breguet-Dorand machine, piloted by Maurice Claisse, had eclipsed these with the following performances:

22 December 1935, speed of 61 mph (98 km/hr);

26 September 1936, height of 158 m (518 ft)*;

24 November 1936, endurance of 1 hr 2 min 5 sec; and distance in a closed circuit of 44 km (27·34 miles).

Apart from advancing helicopter performance in these spheres, the Breguet-Dorand also, after a little early evidence of instability, exhibited good characteristics of controllability, and in 1937 (after a similar achievement by the Fw 61 in Germany) it made its first 'engine off' landing using autorotation. It is

not certain whether the Bugatti engine was ever installed; the aircraft did most or all of its flying with the more powerful Hispano engine. It continued to carry out useful experimental work up to the outbreak of World War 2, but was destroyed in 1943 during an Allied air attack on the airfield at Villacoublay where it was housed.

13 Focke-Wulf Fw 61

As a class of vehicle the helicopter had no single inventor, any more than the fixed-wing aeroplane did. Much of the credit for the modern helicopter goes, deservedly, to Igor Sikorsky; but in Britain, France, Italy, Germany and the USSR contemporaries of Sikorsky all produced significant designs well before the historic VS-300 had left the ground.

High on the short list of helicopter pioneers must come the name of Professor Henrich Karl Johann Focke, whose Fw 61 made its first free flight, lasting 45 seconds,* on 26 June 1936. This was, coincidentally, exactly one year after the less-publicised flight of the Breguet-Dorand aircraft, which can thus claim to have been the first really practical helicopter to have flown in Europe. But the Fw 61, once it had begun to fly, rapidly proved itself a much superior machine to the Breguet, not only as regards performance but as a practical basic design capable of much further development.

---

*But note the height of 1,985 ft (605 m) attained by the Russian TsAGI 1-EA in 1932 (page 105).

* Often given as 28 seconds, but Prof Focke's own log book indicates that the first two flights each lasted 45 seconds.

Focke's first experience of rotor-craft construction and operation was gained from building the Cierva C.19 and C.30 Autogiros under licence, and then in 1934 he built and flew successfully a scale model helicopter that rose to a height of some 18 m (59 ft). There followed a period of research into, and testing of, rotor and transmission systems before, in 1936, the Fw 61 prototype made its appearance.

Registered D-EBVU, the Fw 61 V1 (Werke Nummer 931) utilised the fuselage and Sh.14A engine of a Focke-Wulf Fw 44 Stieglitz basic trainer, with the tailplane mounted on top of the fin and the propeller cut down to the diameter of the engine cylinders to serve purely as a cooling fan. It gave no assistance to the aircraft in forward flight, though its presence may have led the Hungarian engineer von Asboth to believe that the Fw 61 was really an autogyro, for he vehemently challenged the helicopter records (see below) set up by the German machine. Focke confirmed, however, that not only were these all genuine helicopter flights, but that every landing was made vertically. The twin rotors, mounted on steel-tube outriggers on each side of the cabin, were fully-articulated 3-blade assemblies whose blade angle could be increased or decreased so as to provide lateral movement of the aeroplane by creating a lift differential between one side and the other. On 10 May 1937, some months before a similar feat was accomplished by the Breguet-Dorand helicopter, the Fw 61 made

its first landing using autorotation, and in February 1938 the aircraft's controllability was convincingly demonstrated by Germany's celebrated aviatrix Hanna Reitsch, who flew the machine inside the Deutschlandhalle sports stadium in Berlin. Meanwhile a second prototype, D-EKRA, had been completed, and from mid-1937 the Fw 61 established the following list of FAI world records for helicopters:

25/26 June 1937 (pilot Ewald Rohlfs):
2,439 m (8,001·95 ft) altitude (V1);
1 hr 20 min 49 sec endurance (V1);
80·604 km (50·085 miles) distance in a closed circuit (V2);
122·553 km/hr (76·151 mph) speed over a 20 km closed circuit;
16·40 km (10·19 miles) distance in a straight line (V2).

25 October 1937 (pilot Hanna Reitsch):
108·974 km (67·713 miles) distance in a straight line (V2).

19 June 1938 (pilot Karl Bode):
230·248 km (143·069 miles) distance in a straight line.

29 January 1939 (pilot Karl Bode):
3,427 m (11,243·44 ft) altitude.

By the time that the June 1937 records were established, Prof Focke had left Focke-Wulf to form a new company, Focke-Achgelis & Co GmbH, at Delmenhorst/Oldenburg to further the development of the Fw 61 and its derivatives. The obvious promise in the Fw 61's basic design led to a development contract for a 5/6-passenger aerial taxi helicopter for Deutsche Lufthansa. This was one of several proposed variants of the Fa 223 (described separately), and was known as the Fa 266 Hornisse (Hornet). Three prototypes were under construction in mid-1939, but were scrapped after the outbreak of World War 2.

14   Sikorsky VS-300

Russian-born Igor Sikorsky built his first helicopter, powered by a 25 hp Anzani engine, in 1909. It would not leave the ground, and a second machine, completed in 1910, was little better; it did rise a short distance, but was incapable of lifting a pilot, and Sikorsky turned his attention to fixed-wing aeroplanes. After the 1917 Revolution he left the country, settling in the United States some two years later, and soon entering the aircraft industry of his new country. In 1938, when he was Engineering Manager of the Vought-Sikorsky Division of United Aircraft Corporation, years of study and research into rotary-wing flight problems were rewarded when the directors of UAC agreed to let him try once again to build a practical helicopter. The VS-300, as the project was named, was designed during the spring and built during the summer of 1939, and on 14 September Sikorsky was at the controls when the aircraft made its first vertical take-off. At this stage the aircraft was still tethered to the ground and had weights suspended underneath it to help keep it stable. It was powered by a 4-cylinder Lycoming engine of 75 hp, had full cyclic pitch control for the 28 ft (8·53 m) diameter main rotor and a single anti-torque tail rotor at the end of a narrow enclosed tailboom which also supported a large underfin. The cyclic control was not fully satisfactory, however, and was temporarily discarded. By the time the VS-300 made its first free flight on 13 May 1940 (then powered by a 90 hp Franklin motor) the configuration had changed to an open-framework steel-tube fuselage with outriggers at the tail end. Each of these mounted a 6 ft 8 in (2·03 m) diameter horizontally-rotating airscrew to provide better lateral control; the vertical tail screw was retained. By mid-1940 the VS-300 was staying airborne for 15 min at a time, and on 6 May 1941 it beat the world endurance record held by the Fw 61 by staying aloft for 1 hr 32 min 26·1 sec. Various modifications were made during 1940–41, the most important being the restoration of a cyclic pitch control system and the replacement of the tail outriggers in June 1941 by a short vertical pylon carrying a single horizontal tail rotor, and the reinstatement in December of a now fully satisfactory cyclic pitch control for the main rotor. Other alterations concerned the arrangement of the main undercarriage and the fitting of nose and tail wheels in place of skids. In April 1941 Sikorsky made a successful take-off from water by fitting pneumatic flotation bags under the main undercarriage wheels. In its final form the VS-300 had a 150 hp Franklin engine, a fabric-covered fuselage and a tricycle undercarriage. Testing continued throughout 1942 (by which time development of Sikorsky's first production helicopter, the R-4, was well advanced), and in 1943 the VS-300 was delivered to the Henry Ford Museum in Dearborn, Michigan, where it is still housed today.

The first practical helicopters, in the sense that they accomplished satisfactorily manoeuvres that we now take for granted – vertical take-off and landing, hovering, and forward, backward and sideways flight – were the Breguet-Dorand and the Fw 61. The VS-300 accomplished more, by paving the way for production aircraft that could carry a useful load and perform a productive job of work. The general manager of Sikorsky Aircraft, Lee S. Johnson, summed up its contribution twenty years later when he said: 'Before Igor Sikorsky flew the VS-300, there was no helicopter industry; after he flew it, there was.'

15 Flettner Fl 282 Kolibri (Humming-Bird)

The pioneer work of Anton Flettner is often overshadowed by the more publicised activities of his contemporaries Focke and Sikorsky; yet Flettner's first fully practical helicopter, the Fl 265, was far superior to the Fw 61 and made a successful free flight several months before the VS-300 began tethered flights. Flettner's first rotorcraft, flown in 1932, had a 2-blade rotor 98 ft (29·87 m) in diameter, with a 30 hp Anzani engine mounted part of the way along each blade driving a propeller – a form of propulsion similar to that used by the Italian

Vittorio Isacco on his so-called 'helicogyres'. The Flettner machine made a successful tethered take-off, but later overturned during a gale and was written off. The next significant design was the Fl 184 single-seat autogyro; powered by a 150 hp Sh 14 radial engine, it flew in 1935 and was due to be evaluated by the German Navy when it, too, was unfortunately destroyed. The next design was the Fl 185, whose prototype (D-EFLT) flew in 1936 and had a 3-blade main rotor. The centrally-mounted Sh 14A engine drove, in addition to the rotor, two small anti-torque propellers on outriggers each side of the cabin and a large cooling fan in the nose.

By this time, however, Flettner had developed the idea of counter-rotating, intermeshing twin rotors. Many of his advisers thought that the airflow disturbed by the inter-meshing blades would make this system less efficient than one using a single rotor; but Flettner believed that any problems thus encountered would be more than offset by the reduced drag resulting from having no external rotor-carrying structure. He proved his point by installing such a system in the Fl 265, whose prototype (D-EFLV) flew in May 1939. At this time encouragement for the development of small helicopters came mostly from the German Navy, on whose behalf six Fl 265's had been ordered in 1938 with a view to developing a machine suitable for shipboard reconnaissance and anti-submarine patrol. Service trials of the Fl 265 were more than satisfactory, and plans were made for series production; but by this time work was well advanced on a later model, the Fl 282, which could carry 2 men and was more versatile. The RLM therefore agreed to wait for the Fl 282, to hasten whose development it ordered thirty prototypes and fifteen pre-production aircraft in spring 1940. Maiden flight was made in 1941. The first three prototypes were completed as single-seaters and had fully enclosed cabins made up of a series of optically flat Plexiglas panels, faired-in rotor pylons and well-contoured fuselages. The Fl 282 V3 was fitted with endplate auxiliary fins and a long underfin beneath the rear fuselage. Later machines had more utilitarian bodies and some had semi-enclosed cockpits; others, like the example illustrated, had a completely open pilot's seat.

Like the Fl 265, the Fl 282 underwent exhaustive service trials, and several were used operationally from 1942. Usually they flew from platforms above the gun turrets of convoy escort vessels in the Baltic, Aegean and Mediterranean, often in extreme weather conditions, and revealed control and performance qualities well above expectations. By VE-day, only three of the twenty-four prototypes completed by Flettner at Johannisthal still survived, the others having been destroyed to prevent capture. Two of these, the V15 and V23, were taken to the United States, and the other to the Soviet Union. The RLM had placed an order in 1944 for one thousand Fl 282's from BMW, but Allied bombing attacks prevented production from being started.

At least two other Flettner helicopters were under development when the war ended. These were the Fl 285, another fleet spotter with an Argus As 10C engine, capable of making a 2-hour flight and carrying two small bombs; and the Fl 339, a large transport helicopter project powered by a BMW 132A engine.

16 **Doblhoff WNF 342**
First helicopter in the world to take off and land using blade-tip jets to drive the rotor, the WNF 342 was the work of three engineers – Baron Friedrich von Doblhoff, A. Stepan and Theodor Laufer – at the Wiener Neustädter Flugzeugwerke in Vienna. Doblhoff first built, in 1942, a ground test rig to prove the principle of his proposed rotor drive system, this rig consisting basically of a trio of hollow rotor blades mounted on a scaffold with the fuel/air mixture fed through each blade to a small jet unit at the tip. The demonstration proved so successful that the rotor actually 'took off' from its moorings, lifting about a yard into the air an anvil that had been attached to it to hold it down. Encouraged by this success, Doblhoff and his team then applied the principle in the small single-seat WNF 342 V1 which he hoped would meet a German Navy requirement for an observation helicopter to be carried by submarines or small naval vessels. This first prototype, powered by a 60 hp Walter Mikron II engine, was flown in spring 1943. The airframe, constructed

from welded steel tube and fabric covered, had a gross weight of 360 kg (794 lb), twin tail fins and a tricycle undercarriage. Flight testing revealed the need for rather more side area, but performance was otherwise satisfactory, and when the WNF factory was damaged during an Allied air attack in mid-August 1943 the aircraft was moved to a safer site west of Vienna, at Obergraffendorf. Here a second prototype, the WNF 342 V2, was built; this was somewhat heavier at 460 kg (1,014 lb) gross weight, despite its open-framework fuselage, and had a 90 hp engine. The main difference lay in the sail-like tail unit, this comprising a large single rectangular fin and an elongated rudder pivoting about a horizontal axis.

Experience with the first two machines showed that the high fuel consumption of the tip-jets would make the WNF 342's operating costs prohibitive, and so a major design change was introduced in the V3 and V4 prototypes. The tip-drive system was retained for take-off, hovering and landing only, a selective clutch enabling the engine (now a 140 hp BMW-Bramo Sh 14A radial) to drive either the air compressor for jet propulsion or a conventional pusher propeller for forward flight while the rotor blades 'freewheeled' in autorotative pitch. To clear this propeller the rotor pylon was raised above the cabin and the tail unit was redesigned as a twin-boom assembly, that of the V3 carrying two endplate oval fins and rudders while that of the V4 had a single fin and rudder mounted on the tailplane centre-line. Gross weight of the V3, a single-seater with 9·88 m (32 ft 5 in) diameter rotors, was 548 kg (1,208 lb). The V4 had side-by-side open cockpits for a crew of 2. The V3 was destroyed early in its test programme by ground resonance vibration, but the V4 had completed 25 hours of testing before, in April 1945, it was hastily taken westwards to prevent its capture by the advancing Soviet forces. It eventually fell into American hands, Doblhoff later accompanying it back to the United States to assist with further tests.

17 Focke-Achgelis Fa 223 Drache (Dragon)

A helicopter with extremely advanced capabilities for its time, the Fa 223 was fundamentally an extension of the concept which had produced the smaller Fw 61 and employed a generally similar arrangement of twin counter-rotating rotors mounted on outriggers from the main airframe and driven by a fuselage-mounted radial engine. In the case of the Fa 223, however, the engine was installed amidships in the fabric-covered steel-tube fuselage to the rear of the 4-seat passenger compartment. The forward part of this cabin was a multiple-panelled enclosure made up of flat Plexiglas panels, and the aircraft was fitted with a tricycle undercarriage. Usual powerplant was a 1,000 hp Bramo 323 Q-3 radial engine.

The Fa 223 originated in the late 1930s as an experimental design, of which several variants were planned.

One of these was the Fa 266 Hornisse, referred to in the description of the Fw 61. It was to be powered by an 840 hp Bramo engine, and estimated performance included a maximum speed of 118 mph (190 km/hr) and a rate of climb of 1,575 ft/min (8 m/sec). Although none of the three Fa 266 prototypes was completed, another prototype (D-OCEB) was completed in autumn 1939; this was the Fa 223 V1, which by then had been adopted for a military role. Manufacturer's trials with the Fa 223 V1 revealed slight instability at the lower end of the speed range, but the helicopter's general handling and controllability were excellent and on 28 October 1940 D-OCEB was flown to a record height of 7,100 m (23,294 ft). Official acceptance trials in early 1942 were followed by an order for one hundred Fa 223E production helicopters; by July a second prototype (D-OCEW) had flown, but the ten other Fa 223's completed that year were destroyed by Allied air attack. Further raids in July 1944 destroyed six of the eight additional aircraft then completed and flown, together with all others under assembly. The only other example to be built was one completed at a new Berlin factory set up to build Fa 223's at the rate of four hundred per month for the German armed forces, and by VE-day only three airworthy Fa 223's survived. One of these, flown in September 1945 to the Airborne Forces Experimental Establishment in southern England, became the first helicopter to fly the English Channel, exactly seventeen years after the first rotorcraft crossing by the Cierva C.8L Autogiro. Unfortunately, on only its third test flight in Britain, it was written off when it crashed from 60 ft (18 m) after a vertical take-off.

Three known examples were completed after the end of World War 2, all from captured or salvaged components. One of these was built, with the assistance of Professor Henrich Focke, by the SNCA du Sud-Est in France with the designation S.E. 3000 and flown on 23 October 1948. The other pair, designated VR-1, were built at the Ceskoslovenské Závody Letecké (formerly Avia) factory in Czechoslovakia. Uncompleted German wartime projects included proposals to produce a 4-rotor helicopter by joining two Fa 223's together in tandem with a new fuselage centre-section; and the much larger Fa 284 crane helicopter to be powered by two 1,600 or 2,000 hp BMW engines and capable in the latter form of lifting a 7,000 kg (15,432 lb) payload.

18 Bratukhin Omega series

As recorded elsewhere in this volume, Ivan P. Bratukhin was one of the pioneer figures in Soviet rotorcraft development and a senior member of the division formed under Boris N. Yuriev at the TsAGI (Central Aero and Hydrodynamic Institute) to carry out research into problems associated with rotary-winged flight. Rotorcraft development at the TsAGI suffered various political and economic setbacks during the late 1930s, but a new phase of development began, with Bratukhin in charge, in spring 1940, from which the Omega helicopters were the first significant products to emerge.

Design of the Omega was strongly influenced by the success in Germany of the little Fw 61, and the Soviet machine adopted a similar layout of twin rotors mounted on lateral outriggers on the main fuselage, the most significant difference being that the Omega 2MG, as the first prototype was called, had twin engines. These were MV-6 inlines, each of 220 hp and each mounted in a rectangular pod at the end of one of the outriggers beneath the 7·00 m (22 ft 11⅝ in) diameter 3-blade rotors. The Omega 2MG, completed in August 1941, made its first free flight in early 1943 and exhibited generally satisfactory qualities, most of the troubles encountered being due to an inferior powerplant. The Omega II, built in 1944, was therefore basically similar except in using a pair of 350 hp MG-41F radials. This machine was one of a small batch of Omega helicopters displayed publicly at Tushino airfield in August 1946, by which time it had completed its test programme and was being used as an instructional aircraft.

Meanwhile construction had been started of the next Omega development, the G-3, using 450 hp Pratt & Whitney R-985-AN-1 engines. Two prototype and five pre-production G-3's were built, but the G-4 was then preferred because it used the more readily available domestic AI-26 engine. The G-4, with bigger rotors, was slower than the G-3 in forward flight but had a far superior altitude performance. The first of two prototype G-4's was flown in October 1947, and four more pre-production aircraft were built before further Omega development was curtailed in 1948. Three subsequent Bratukhin designs – the 6-passenger B-5, the B-9 ambulance and B-10 observation helicopter – all used the Omega design as a basis, differing chiefly in having improved fuselages and fixed wings to off-load the rotors. These carried out ground tests but none made a free flight. Two B-11 prototypes were also built and flown in 1948, but their vibration troubles were never completely eradicated and the design was abandoned in the late spring of 1950. When the Bratukhin team was disbanded in 1951 other designs under development included one for a compound helicopter, not unlike the Kamov Ka-22.

19 Sikorsky R-4

The Sikorsky R-4, or VS-316A, was a definitive development of Igor Sikorsky's successful pre-war VS-300, and in 1944 became the first helicopter in the world to be placed in series production. Like the VS-300, it had a framework of heavy-gauge steel tube, and all but the extreme rear end of the fuselage was fabric-covered, as were the 36 ft (10·97 m) diameter main rotor blades. A completely new feature was the fully-enclosed cabin, with side-by-side seating and dual controls for the 2-man crew. Powered by a 165 hp Warner R-500-3 engine, the prototype VS-316A flew for the first time on 14 January 1942; later, with the military designation XR-4 and serial number 41-18874, the aircraft was handed over to the USAAF for evaluation. It arrived at Wright Field, Ohio, on 18 May 1942, having completed, in stages, the 761 mile (1,225 km) trip from Bridgeport, Connecticut, in 16 hr 10 min flying time. Later in 1942 an order was placed for three service test YR-4A's with 180 hp R-550-1 engines and main rotors of 38 ft (11·58 m) diameter, and similar changes were made to the XR-4 in 1943, after which it was redesignated XR-4C. Other 1943 developments included the first-ever landing by a helicopter on a ship at sea (the tanker *Bunker Hill*) and the production of twenty-seven pre-series YR-4B's for further evaluation by the USAAF, the US Navy (three) and the RAF (seven). These were generally similar to the YR-4A's except for an enlarged cabin, and were used inter alia for winterisation and tropical trials in Alaska and Burma. In the latter theatre one of the YR-4B's carried out the first recorded casualty evacuation operation by helicopter.

One hundred production R-4B's were ordered by the USAAF, similar to the YR-4B except for a 200 hp engine and increased range; twenty of these, and two others, were delivered to the US Navy as HNS-1 aircraft for air/sea rescue duties with the US Coast Guard and for the training of helicopter pilots. A batch of forty-five was supplied to Great Britain under Lend-Lease, most of them going to the Royal Navy. The R-4B was known in British service as the Hoverfly I. In the RAF it replaced the Rota (Cierva C.30A) Autogiros of No 529 Squadron from August 1944, and some were supplied to the Helicopter Training School at Andover in early 1945. By the end of the year the type had passed out of RAF service, some aircraft being allocated for radar calibration work with the Telecommunications Research Establishment; others undertook snow and flood reporting duties, and one was allocated to The King's Flight to carry mail and freight. The Joint Experimental Helicopter Unit, established in 1954, was equipped initially with R-4B and R-6A helicopters handed on from the Royal Air Force and Fleet Air Arm. The R-4 did not enjoy a long service career, either in Britain or the United States, being supplanted in the early post-war years by the Sikorsky S-51 and its British-built equivalent, the Westland Dragonfly. Those still in American service were redesignated H-4B in 1948.

20 **Sikorsky R-6**
Ordered in 1943, the Sikorsky XR-6 prototype (43-47955) made its maiden flight on 15 October 1943. As its manufacturer's designation (VS-316B) indicated, it began as a refined and developed version of the R-4 (VS-316A), and the same rotor and transmission system was used in both types. A 225 hp Lycoming O-435-7 engine provided the power,

and the fuselage was transformed into a streamlined, tadpole-shaped unit with a frameless moulded Plexiglas cabin for the 2 crew members. On 2 March 1944 the XR-6 set new helicopter distance, endurance and altitude records when it made a non-stop flight of 387 miles (623 km) from Washington, DC, to Dayton, Ohio, in 4 hr 55 min, climbing to 5,000 ft (1,524 m) over the Allegheny Mountains en route. The XR-6 was followed by five 2-seat service test XR-6A's for the USAAF and US Navy, built by Sikorsky with 240 hp Franklin O-405-9 engines, and twenty-six generally similar pre-production YR-6A's built by the Nash-Kelvinator Corporation. The latter company was also awarded the production contract for one hundred and ninety-three R-6A's; work on these began in 1945, but not all of them are known to have been completed. Thirty-six were delivered to the US Navy as the HOS-1, plus three of the XR-6A's redesignated as XHOS-1's, and formed the equipment of that service's first helicopter squadron (VX-3), which commissioned in July 1946. They seem to have been employed primarily on air/sea rescue duties. A number of R-6A's were supplied to Britain under Lend–Lease, these being named Hoverfly II in British service. Details are not wholly conclusive, but only about twenty-seven of these appear to have been assembled and used in service, including two by the Royal Navy. Principal RAF units were No 657 (AOP) Squadron and the Airborne Forces Experimental Establishment.

Like the R-4, the R-6 could be fitted with pontoons as an alternative to a wheeled landing gear. Its career was a short one: it was frequently beset by engine difficulties, and soon gave way to the more reliable R-5 and its derivatives. A proposed Lycoming-powered R-6B version by Nash-Kelvinator was cancelled, but this designation may later have been applied to some aircraft believed to have been used by the US Coast Guard.

21   **Bristol 171 Sycamore**
First post-war British commercial helicopter, the Type 171 was also the first venture by Bristol Aeroplane Co into the field of rotorcraft. Design studies, under Raoul Hafner, were started in June 1944 and, since no suitable British engine was available at that time, the two Mk 1 prototypes (VL958 and VL963) were built with 450 hp Pratt & Whitney R-985 Wasp Junior radial engines. These were 4-seaters, conforming to Ministry of Supply Specification E.20/45; VL958 was first flown on 27 July 1947, and VL963 in early 1948. A Certificate of Airworthiness – the first awarded to a British helicopter – was granted on 25 April 1949. These events were followed by the flight on 3 September 1949 of the one and only Mk 2, built as a 4-seater to Specification E.34/46 and powered by a 550 hp Alvis Leonides 71 piston engine.

This aircraft formed the basis for the first production series, all of which had the nose shortened to improve downward vision and the fuselage width increased to permit bench seating of 3 passengers behind the flight crew. Detail modifications were also made to machines within these batches, some of which were to become standard on later production aircraft. The first two production batches, totalling twenty-five aircraft, included one HC Mk 10 ambulance for evaluation by the Army Air Corps; four HC Mk 11's for Army communications work; four HR Mk 12's for RAF communications and ASR duties, evaluated by Coastal Command; and two winch-equipped HR Mk 13's for similar trials with Fighter Command. These were collectively to Mk 3 production standard, with 520 hp Leonides 173 engines. Two Mk 3A's, with improved performance, and extra baggage space behind the engine bay, were completed for British European Airways. Of the remaining dozen machines, five were to Mk 4 standard, also with Leonides 173 engines and having four cabin doors, a taller landing gear, and the pilot seated, American-fashion, on the starboard side; these were built for the Royal Australian Navy (three HR Mk 50), Royal Australian Air Force (one) and RAF (one HR Mk 14). The remaining seven aircraft were a mixture of Mks 3 and 4 reserved for military trials or civil demonstration.

Subsequent output of the Sycamore, as the military Bristol 171 was known, brought the overall total to one hundred and seventy-seven, before production ended in 1959. A further eighty-five HR Mk 14's were built, including a second Sycamore for the RAAF (for use at the Woomera rocket range) and three employed by the Force Aérienne Belge in the (then Belgian) Congo. Seven more Sycamores, designated HC Mk 51, were delivered to the Royal Australian Navy, and fifty Mk 52's were supplied to the Federal German forces for miscellaneous duties. Most of these were for Army use, although four were allocated to the Bundesmarine. The first Sycamores in RAF service were those delivered to No 275 Squadron in April 1953, others joining No 194 Squadron in Malaya in 1954 and No 284 in Cyprus in late 1956. Sycamores have also served in such other trouble spots as Kenya and Aden, and have performed a wide variety of rescue or support duties in addition to liaison work. In the civil field Bristol 171's have performed mountain rescue, traffic patrol and mining survey work, and in August 1955 an aircraft of this type took part in the first British air-to-ground television transmission involving the use of a helicopter. One of the Mk 3 trials aircraft, WT933, was flown with increased fin area in 1958 to provide aerodynamic background for the proposed turbine-powered Bristol 203. Components from the incomplete 179th and 180th Sycamore airframes were embodied in the part-built prototype of this 11-seat helicopter before the project was abandoned.

22 Sikorsky R-5, S-51 and Westland Dragonfly

The origins of this long-serving helicopter date back to the VS-372 design, begun in early 1943 to meet a USAAF requirement for an observation helicopter bigger and with a better performance than the Sikorsky R-4. It retained a similar powerplant and rotor system, but the fuselage was an entirely new design with a reversed tricycle undercarriage and seating 2 crew members in tandem. Five XR-5 prototypes of this design were eventually ordered and the first of these (43-28236) was flown on 18 August 1943 powered by a 450 hp R-985-AN-5 Wasp Junior engine. The USAAF subsequently received twenty-six pre-series YR-5A's and thirty-four production R-5A's. Five of the former were later converted to dual control YR-5E's, and twenty-one of the latter to R-5D's with 600 hp R-1340 engines, nosewheel undercarriage, a rescue hoist, extra fuel tank and a third occupant. Two of the R-5A's were delivered to the US Navy as HO2S-1's.

A developed version of the R-5D, having a nosewheel undercarriage but retaining the Wasp Junior engine with a slightly larger rotor, became the 4-passenger S-51, produced originally for the commercial market and flown for the first time on 16 February 1946. Certification by the CAA was received during the following month and in August 1946 the first customer delivery was made. In 1947 the USAF received eleven military S-51's designated R-5F; these were followed in 1948–49 by thirty-nine H-5G's with rescue hoists and maximum take-off weight increased from 6,200 lb (2,812 kg) to 6,500 (2,948 kg) and sixteen

similar H-5H's with amphibious wheel/pontoon landing gear. About ninety military S-51's were supplied to the US Navy as HO3S-1's and -2's.

Sikorsky production of the R-5/S-51 series, which ended in 1951, totalled some three hundred aircraft. The USAF machines were employed primarily by the Air Rescue Service, carrying an enclosed stretcher externally on each side of the cabin. The US Navy's HO3S's served principally on plane guard and general observation duties, and performed particularly well during the Korean War of 1950-53.

In December 1946 Westland Aircraft Ltd began a long acquaintance with Sikorsky by acquiring a licence to build the S-51 in Great Britain. Following the import of a batch of six as demonstration and pattern aircraft, the first Westland-built WS-51 (G-AKTW) was flown on 5 October 1948, and from then until 1953 Westland turned out one hundred and thirty-nine examples of the S-51 variants, mostly for the British services, with 520 hp Alvis Leonides engines. These aircraft were given the name Dragonfly. Early models with rotor blades of composite construction were designated HR Mk 1 (thirteen for the Royal Navy, first flown 22 June 1949) and HC Mk 2 (three for the RAF). Corresponding versions with all-metal blades were fifty-eight HR Mk 3 for the Navy and twelve HC Mk 4 for the RAF. The first Navy Dragonflies, which entered service in 1950, were allocated to No 705

Squadron, the first all-helicopter squadron to be formed outside the United States. They performed plane guard, air/sea rescue, communications and photographic duties, and most were brought up to HR Mk 5 standard from 1957 with increased engine power and equipment changes. The RAF Dragonflies, employed primarily in the ambulance role, served with the Far East Casualty Evacuation Flight (later No 194 Squadron) based in Malaya from 1950–56. Most civil WS-51's were Leonides-engined Mk 1A's, though the Mk 1B was offered with the American powerplant if required. Westland Dragonflies were sold to Belgium (three for Sabena), the Royal Ceylon Air Force (two), Egyptian Air Force (two), French Air Force (nine), Royal Iraqi Air Force (two), Italian Air Force (three), Japan (three for the Air Self-Defence Force and two for Tohuku Electric), Royal Thai Air Force (four) and Yugoslav Air Force (ten). Some of the Sikorsky-built S-51 demonstrators were allocated for a time to British European Airways, which on 1 June 1950 inaugurated with these aircraft the first regular helicopter passenger service in the world, between Liverpool and Cardiff.

In 1955, Westland introduced an S-51 conversion known as the Widgeon. This had a redesigned cabin, with small clamshell nose doors and accommodation for 4 passengers; a 520 hp Leonides 521 engine; and an S-55-type rotor head and 4-blade main rotor. First flight was made on 23 August 1955 by G-AKTW, converted to Widgeon standard, and Westland subsequently produced fifteen Widgeons for the air forces of Ceylon (two) and Jordan (one), the Brazilian Navy (three), the Hong Kong Police Department (two) and civil customers. A proposal to convert twenty-four Royal Navy helicopters to Widgeon standard as Dragonfly HR Mk 7's was not adopted.

23   Sud-Aviation SO 1221 Djinn

The Djinn was the world's first production helicopter to make use of the 'cold jet' principle of propulsion. The term 'cold jet' indicates simply that compressed air from the gas turbine engine is ducted through channels inside the rotor blades and expelled through nozzles at their tips without further combustion; the air itself is in fact warm enough to eliminate the need for other means of de-icing the blades. No tail rotor is fitted, the aircraft having two outrigged fins and a large central rudder that is situated in the line of the residual thrust exhaust from the engine to provide directional control. The Djinn is a highly manoeuvrable little machine, and has been described as 'lenient where flying faults are concerned'.

The Djinn's career began with two single-seat SO 1220 prototypes, F-WGVO and F-WGZX, the first of which made its maiden flight on 2 January 1953. These were both intended primarily to prove the rotor and propulsion systems, and were open-framework machines without enclosed cabins; F-WGVO was later fitted experimentally with agricultural spray booms. On 16 December 1953 the first of five 2-seat SO 1221 prototypes was flown, having a fully enclosed cabin and an all-up weight of 600 kg (1,323 lb), and on 29 December this aircraft established a new altitude record in its class of 4,789 m (15,712 ft). Twenty-two pre-series SO 1221's were then built, primarily for evaluation for the French Army, and the first of these was flown on 23 September 1954. Three machines from this batch were evaluated by the US Army, under the designation YHO-1DJ.

Chief customer for the Djinn was France's Aviation Légère de l'Armée de Terre, which received one hundred of the one hundred and fifty production Djinns completed up to 1961. Six were delivered to the Federal German Heeresfliegerei. The military Djinns operate at slightly higher gross weight – 800 kg (1,764 lb) – than the civil models. One was used in France for the first experiments in launching Nord SS.10 anti-tank missiles from a helicopter, but the Djinn's main military functions have been those of observation, liaison, training and (with one pilot and two external litters) casualty evacuation. During the late 1960s, between forty and fifty civil Djinns were active in ten countries, most of them in an agricultural role, for which Sud-Aviation offered renewed conversion facilities in 1965. The so-called 'agricopter' version of the Djinn can carry up to 200 litres (44 Imp gal) of liquid chemical in twin tanks, and is fitted with lateral spray bars for the spraying, dusting or 'fogging' of crops with fertilisers or pesticides.

24 Westland (Saunders-Roe) Skeeter

After a development period spanning some ten years, production examples of the Saro Skeeter finally began their career in 1958, with the British Army Air Corps. This attractive little 2-seater had originated as a Cierva design, the W.14 Skeeter 1, whose prototype (G-AJCJ) flew for the first time on 8 October 1948 powered by a 106 hp Jameson FF-1 engine. A second aircraft, the Skeeter 2 G-ALUF, was flown on 15 October 1949, in which the most important of several design changes were the employment of a 145 hp Gipsy Major 10 engine, increased rotor diameter and a slightly longer tail-boom of circular instead of tri-angular cross-section. Two further-modified Skeeter 3's, to Specification A. 13/49, were begun by Cierva, with Gipsy Major 8's; these were completed by Saro, for evaluation by the Ministry of Supply, after the latter company had acquired Cierva in January 1951. About a year later they were given 180 hp Blackburn Bombardier 702 engines and re-designated Skeeter 3B's; one similar machine was completed, to meet a Royal Navy requirement, as the Skeeter 4.

Saro's Skeeter 5 prototype, built as a private venture, also had Bombardier engines, and was the first of the series to be really free of the ground resonance problems which had beset the earlier prototypes. It was followed by three Skeeter 6 prototypes with 183 hp Gipsy Major 200 Mk 30's, and in 1955 the Skeeter 5 also changed to this brand of engine.

After pre-service trials with the Skeeter 6 prototypes, four more evaluation aircraft were ordered, these emerging as three AOP Mk 10's and one T Mk 11 dual-control trainer. The major production version, of which sixty-four were built, was the AOP Mk 12 for the Army Air Corps. Delivery of these was made between spring 1958 and autumn 1960. Some, fitted with dual controls, were used by the RAF to train Army helicopter instructors. These were designated T Mk 12, although sometimes known as T Mk 13. The Skeeter was also the subject of a small export order, the Federal German Army and Navy receiving six and four as Mks 50 and 51 respectively. Final variant was the Skeeter 8, basically an adaptation of the 7 for commercial operation. Three were laid down for C of A tests, but only one was completed and no civil orders ensued. Skeeter production came to an end in 1960, by which time Saunders-Roe had become part of the Westland group.

Of the Skeeters supplied to the British services, the AOP 12's served mostly at the Army Corps Training School. The German Skeeters were handed over in July 1961 to the Fôrça Aérea Portuguesa. During their early life various Skeeter prototypes were used to flight-test a supercharged Gipsy Major engine, a Blackburn Turmo turboshaft, and a Napier rocket-powered tip-drive system.

25 **Hiller Model 12/H-23 Raven**
In 1944, at the age of 18, Stanley Hiller Junr designed and built his first helicopter, the XH-44. This aircraft (NX30033) was America's first helicopter successfully to employ co-axial twin rotors, but after a year or two studying this and similar designs Hiller began to seek something lighter and cheaper. He therefore turned to a single main rotor layout in a design known as the United Helicopters UH-5, and in this machine also developed the 'Rotor-Matic' rotor control system which was installed in his first production helicopter.

Known originally as the Hiller Model 360, this appeared in 1948 as a 3-seater, powered by a 178 hp Franklin 6V4-178-B33 and having a fully enclosed fuselage and cabin. This structure was simplified on the production version, known as the Model 12, which retained the enclosed tailboom but had an open cockpit and engine bay. The Model 12 received FAA Type Approval on 14 October 1948 and in 1949 an aircraft of this type made the first trans-continental flight in the USA by a commercial helicopter. With new-type rotor blades and minor modifications the 1950 version became the Model 12A, later versions of which were powered by 200 hp 6V4-200-C33 or 210 hp 6V-335-B Franklin engines. Single examples of the Model 12A were evaluated by the US Army and Navy, leading to a small order for sixteen HTE-1 trainers for the Navy and a more substantial one for one hundred H-23A Ravens for the Army. In all, one hundred and ninety-four civil and military examples of the Model 12 and 12A were built, including five H-23A's for evaluation by the US Air Force.

Operational experience with the H-23A in Korea led to an improved model, the 12B, four hundred and fifty-three of which were eventually built. Two hundred and seventy-three of these were Army H-23B's including two hundred and sixteen assigned to the Primary Helicopter School at Fort Wolters, Texas, for training. The Model 12B's were powered by 200 or 210 hp Franklin engines and normally had a skid or float landing gear, although a 4-wheel undercarriage was fitted to the US Navy's thirty-five HTE-2's. The major design changes in the 1955 Model 12C (200 hp Franklin) were its all-metal rotor blades and one-piece 'goldfish bowl' cabin hood. Of two hundred civil and military Model 12C's completed, one hundred and forty-five were delivered from 1956 as US Army H-23C's (later redesignated OH-23C). The civil model was certificated by the FAA on 12 December 1955.

The Model 12D, first flown on 3 April 1956, was exclusively a military version, four hundred and eighty-three being built for the US Army as the H-23D (later OH-23D) with 250 hp Lycoming O-540 engines, new rotor transmission and drive

systems, higher gross weight and a substantially longer overhaul life. One additional machine, designated H-23D-2, was fitted with a 305 hp VO-540 Lycoming and used by Hiller to develop the automatic stabilising gear for the later L4.

This engine also powered the Hiller 12E (originally UH-12E). Certificated by the FAA in January 1959, the Hiller 12E was offered in civil form as the L3 with a 305 hp Lycoming VO-540-C2A or as the SL3 with a supercharged 315 hp TIVO-540-A2A engine. Both had the new rotor system and automatic stabilisation equipment. As the OH-23G, the Hiller 12E replaced the OH-23D in US Army service: the final OH-23D contract was amended to specify the G model and a further three hundred and forty-seven OH-23G's were ordered. Twenty-four were supplied to the Canadian Defence Department as the CH-112 Nomad, and twenty-one to the Fleet Air Arm. A 1960 development of the original Hiller 12E was the E4, with a 2 ft 1 in (0·63 m) longer cabin seating 4 people and anhedral stabilisers on the tailboom. Twenty-two of these were purchased by the US Army as OH-23F's for transport during geodetic survey work in Central and South America. Civil models announced in 1963 included the L4 and SL4, with powerplants corresponding to the 3-seat L3 and SL3.

Several hundred Hiller 12E's were exported, to the governments of Argentina, Morocco and Thailand; to the air forces of Bolivia, Chile,

Colombia, Guatemala, Mexico, the Netherlands, Paraguay, Peru and Uruguay. In the civil field the Hiller 12 has been used widely for such duties as crop control, forestry patrol, fire fighting and aerial survey work, as well as private or business transport. Total production of the Hiller 12 range of helicopters passed the two thousand mark before coming to an end in 1965; of these, well over three hundred were exported.

26 **Hughes Model 200 and 300 and TH-55A Osage**
This deceptively slight-looking, ultra-light helicopter has progressively amassed a substantial sales record since the first production machine was delivered in October 1961, and about seventeen hundred examples had been sold by the beginning of 1972. Under its original designation of Model 269 it was initiated as a private venture in September 1955 by the Aircraft Division of the Hughes Tool Company, and N78P, the first of two prototypes, was flown for the first time in October 1956. Powered by a 170 hp Lycoming engine, this machine had a triangular girder-type tailboom, a plain skid landing gear, and accommodated 2 occupants in side-by-side seats.

In 1958 five developed Model 269A's were ordered for evaluation by the US Army under the designation YHO-2HU, the first of these aircraft bearing the serial number 58-1327. Changes from the prototype included replacement of the openwork tailboom by a simple tubular structure, on which a modified stabiliser was mounted further aft and on the starboard side only; widening of the cabin; and the fitting of ground handling wheels at the forward extremities of the landing skids. In this form the helicopter was granted FAA Type Approval on 9 April 1959, and in July 1960 Hughes decided to place the aircraft in production. The basic 2-seat version was the Model 269A, while a 3-seat model was offered as the 269B. The major customer for the 2-seat variant was the US Army which, after thorough evaluation at Fort Rucker, Alabama, selected it as a standard primary light helicopter trainer with a first contract for twenty machines. Orders for the TH-55A Osage eventually totalled seven hundred and ninety-two for the US Army, and similar aircraft are in service with the Algerian Air Force (eight), Brazilian Navy (nine), Colombian Air Force (six), Ghana Air Force (three), Indian Navy (ten), Japan Air SDF (forty-nine), Nicaraguan Air Force (one) and Swedish Army (two). Undoubtedly an important factor in the selection of the Hughes design for the training role was the simplicity of its controls (it has a clutchless, Vee-belt drive) and of its construction and maintenance. Its slender lines belie its sturdy construction, and general handling qualities are said to be excellent. Several hundred 2- and 3-seat models are in world-wide commercial or private operation. A production and marketing licence is held by Bredanardi in Italy.

In 1965 the 2- and 3-seat civil

variants were redesignated, respectively, Models 200 and 300, of which the latter remained current in 1972. It is available with standard or de luxe finish, may be fitted with twin floats in addition to the normal wheel/skid gear, and has a QTR (quiet tail rotor) which reduces the overall noise level by some 80 per cent. A stretcher pannier or two baggage carriers can be fitted externally. The Model 300 (as the Hughes 269B) was certificated by the FAA on 30 December 1963. It differs principally from the Model 200 in having a 180 hp Lycoming HIO-360-A1A engine and a 3-person bench seat, on which the middle occupant sits slightly back from the other two. Also in production, as the Model 300C (originally Model 269C, first flown in August 1969), is a developed version capable of carrying a 45 per cent greater payload. This was certificated in May 1970 and has a 190 hp Lycoming HIO-360-D1A engine, larger main and tail rotors (with lengthened main rotor mast and tailboom), and an enlarged fin. A variant of this, with special communications equipment for police use, was announced in late 1971 with the name Sky Knight.

27 Aérospatiale Alouette II

The Alouette story began with the Sud-Est SE 3101, the first all-French helicopter to be designed and built after World War 2. A single-seater, the SE 3101 was powered by an 85 hp Mathis engine and flew for the first time in June 1948. There then followed the 2-seat SE 3110 (F-WFUE), which had a 200 hp Salmson 9 NH engine. The first of the line to be named Alouette (Lark) was developed originally for an agricultural role. Two SE 3120 prototypes, F-WGGD and 'GE, were completed, also with the Salmson as powerplant, and this type established several world and national helicopter records in July 1953.

The production model, however, was turbine-powered. This was the SE 3130 Alouette II, two prototypes of which were built with Artouste II turboshaft engines. The first SE 3130 was flown on 12 March 1955, and three months later the Alouette II set a new helicopter altitude record of 8,209 m (26,932 ft). Three similar pre-series SE 3130's were completed, and the Alouette II gained its domestic certificate of airworthiness on 2 May 1957. Production Artouste-powered Alouette II's were delivered initially to fulfil orders from the French forces and civilian customers, but when production ended nine hundred and twenty-three had been built for customers in thirty-three countries. Three hundred and sixty-three of these were built for the French services – particularly the Aviation Légère de l'Armée de Terre – and a further two hundred and sixty-seven were built for the Federal German armed forces. Other major military customers for the Alouette II Artouste (which was redesignated SE 313B in 1967) included the Belgian Army (thirty-nine), Swiss Army (thirty), all three Swedish air arms (total twenty-five), and Britain's Army Air Corps (seventeen).

Alouette II Artoustes were also delivered to the air forces of Austria (sixteen), Cambodia (eight), Congo Leopoldville (three), Dominican Republic (two), Indonesia (three), Israel (four), Ivory Coast (two), Laos (two), Lebanon (three), Mexico (two), Morocco (seven), Netherlands (eight), Peru (six), Portugal (seven), South Africa (seven) and Tunisia (eight). Primary military roles are those of observation, photography, air/sea rescue, liaison and training, but the aircraft can be equipped for more belligerent duties. Alouettes of the ALAT have carried out firing trials using Nord AS.10 or AS.11 anti-tank missiles, while some of the Aéronavale's machines have been used to carry homing torpedoes. Other uses include casualty evacuation (with two external stretcher panniers), cropspraying and flying crane (with a 500 kg – 1,100 lb – external sling load). Wheel, skid or pontoon landing gear may be fitted as required to all versions. Licences to assemble and market the Alouette II were granted to Saab in Sweden and Republic in the United States, and in 1963 an Alouette became the first commercially operated turbine helicopter in the USA.

Production of the Alouette has continued in the form of the SA 318C (originally SE 3180), which first flew on 31 January 1961 and received domestic type approval on 18 February 1964. This is basically the same airframe, but with a 530 shp Astazou IIA turboshaft engine (derated to 360 shp) and the strengthened transmission system of the Alouette III. An initial fifteen Alouette II Astazous were built for the ALAT; by the beginning of 1972 orders for this version had reached three hundred and forty-two, for the Gendarmerie, the Federal German police force and many other military and civil customers. On 17 March 1969 the prototype was flown of a new version known as the SA 315B Lama. Essentially, this has a reinforced Alouette II airframe combined with the 870 shp (derated to 550 shp) Artouste IIIB engine, rotor and transmission system of the Alouette III. Developed originally to meet an Indian armed forces requirement, the Lama had totalled sixty-two orders from ten operators by January 1972, and licence production was being undertaken in India by Hindustan Aeronautics Ltd; on 21 June 1972 one of these aircraft set up a new absolute height record for helicopters of 40,815 ft (12,440 m).

28 Silvercraft SH-4

The first helicopter of all-Italian design and construction to receive both Italian and FAA certification, the SH-4 had its origins in a prototype multi-purpose light helicopter, the Silvercraft XY, which was flown for the first time in October 1963. Further development of the XY, initially with financial and technical assistance from SIAI-Marchetti (a shareholder in Silvercraft SpA), led to the first flight by an SH-4 prototype in March 1965. Five pre-series and fifty production SH-4's had been ordered up to 1972, when a further production run of two hundred of these aircraft was to be started. Seating a pilot and 2 passengers, the helicopter is available in three basic versions: the standard general-purpose SH-4 (as illustrated), the agricultural SH-4A (normally operated as a single-seater), and the SH-4C. The standard version can be fitted with Franklin 6A-350 series engines of 200 or 235 hp, in either case derated to 170 hp; the SH-4C offers a supercharged Franklin engine. The 200 hp 6A-350-D1 powers the SH-4A, which can carry twin tanks containing up to 53 US gallons (200 litres) of liquid or 441 lb (200 kg) of dry chemical, the former being dispensed through nozzles in a 32 ft 9½ in (10·00 m) spray bar fitted underneath the cabin. A skid-type landing gear is standard on all versions, but an alternative pontoon gear for amphibious operation may be fitted if required.

29 Mil Mi-1 ('Hare')

Mikhail Leontyevich Mil, who must rank with Igor Sikorsky as one of the world's leading exponents of rotorcraft design, was a contemporary of Nikolai Kamov at the TsAGI (Central Aero and Hydrodynamic Institute) from the early 1930s, and for a time during World War 2 was Technical Officer of the Soviet Air Force's First Rotorcraft Squadron. Given charge of his own design bureau in 1947, he became responsible for the first Soviet helicopter to go into quantity production. Originally designated GM-1, the Mi-1 prototype was completed and flown in September 1948 and

was a compact machine with a fully-enclosed metal-skinned fuselage. It was built to a single main rotor configuration, with a small anti-torque rotor at the rear – a layout to which Mil designs have adhered almost exclusively ever since. The Mi-1 made its public debut at the Tushino Air Display in 1951, by which time it was already in production and service with the Soviet armed forces.

Subsequent production of the Mi-1, both in the Soviet Union and in Poland, was extensive. In addition to those built for the Soviet armed forces, military Mi-1's were also supplied to the DOSAAF and the air forces of Afghanistan, Albania, Algeria, Bulgaria, China, Cuba, Czechoslovakia, Egypt, Finland, Hungary, Iraq, North Korea, Mongolia, Poland and Syria. A wide range of duties include observation, liaison, rescue, ambulance and training. Wide use was also made of the Mi-1 by Aeroflot and by civil authorities in the Soviet Union and other Soviet bloc countries. The standard Mi-1 seats 3 passengers in addition to the pilot; variants include the Mi-1T, which carries only 2 passengers, the Mi-1U dual-control trainer and the Mi-1NKh, a utility model for such duties as freight and mail carriage, ambulance and agricultural operations. Other models to appear were the 1956 Mi-3, a slightly heavier version with a 4-blade main rotor, wider cabin and additional flight aids; and the Mi-1 Moskvich, a refined version of the standard Mi-1, produced for Aeroflot.

Polish production began with the standard Mi-1 in late 1955, this being built at the WSK works at Swidnik under the designation SM-1 with a licence-built version of the AI-26V engine. Several of the Mi-1's supplied to foreign air forces were Polish-built, and subsequent versions included the SM-1W (pilot and 3 passengers), SM-1WS (2-stretcher ambulance), SM-1WZ (agricultural) and SM-1WSZ (dual-control trainer). Production of the Mi-1/SM-1 was probably phased out around 1963 in favour of later turbine-powered developments, but large numbers of these useful little machines are still active in many parts of the world. The SM-2, a Polish development of the basic design, was flown in late 1959 and entered production in 1961. This had a longer nose, thereby enlarging the cabin to accommodate 4 passengers in addition to the pilot or a third stretcher inside the cabin in addition to two carried on external panniers.

30 WSK-Swidnik (Mil) Mi-2 ('Hoplite')

The Mi-2 is basically a turbine-powered development of the Mi-1 in which, by mounting two small turboshaft engines above the fuselage, the entire cabin area can be made available for a payload. First announced in autumn 1961, the Mi-2 was flown for the first time two years later. Designed in the USSR by the Mikhail L.Mil bureau, the Mi-2 was flight-tested in the Soviet Union, but in 1964 the entire future production and development was handed over to the WSK factory at Swidnik in Poland. Production began in 1965, and several hundred had been built by 1972. The Mi-2 is intended for a similar range of light utility duties to those performed by the Mi-1 and in its passenger form can carry 6 or 8 people in addition to the pilot. In the ambulance role it can accommodate 4 stretchers and a medical attendant; as a freighter, it can carry 700 kg (1,543 lb) of cargo. For flying crane or rescue duties it can be fitted with an under-fuselage hook for a sling load of 800 kg (1,764 lb) or a winch over the cabin door capable of lifting up to 120 kg (264 lb). The Mi-2's fourth main application is in the agricultural role, for which it can carry a hopper on either side of the cabin containing 450 kg (992 lb) of dry chemical or 600 litres (132 Imp gallons) of liquid; on non-agricultural Mi-2's these containers can be replaced by additional fuel tanks. A dual-control pilot training version has also been designed. Mi-2's are in service with the Polish Air Force, and are believed to serve also with other air forces such as those of Bulgaria, Hungary, Romania and possibly the Soviet Union.

31 Mil Mi-4 ('Hound')

Design work on the Mi-4 helicopter started in the second half of 1951 and the aircraft was flown in prototype form in August 1952. In appearance it closely resembles the contemporary Sikorsky S-55, but in terms of size and performance it equates with Sikorsky's later S-58. The Mi-4 was already in Soviet Air Force service by August 1953, when it was first seen publicly at the Tushino Aviation Day display, and it has since become the most widely built of all Soviet helicopters. Production is believed to have ceased around 1964, by which time several thousand had been built both in the Soviet Union and in China.

The Mi-4 was produced initially as a troop and assault transport helicopter for the Soviet armed forces. This version is characterised by circular cabin windows and a ventral fairing in which the navigator is stationed. Alternatively an additional fuel tank can be fitted in this position. The Mi-4 has clamshell rear loading doors and can accommodate a maximum freight payload of 1,600 kg (3,527 lb). Typical military loads include 14 fully equipped troops, a GAZ-59 command vehicle, a 76 mm anti-tank gun or 2 motor-cycle combinations. Some have been equipped for an ASW role, with under-nose search radar, an MAD 'bird', and flares, markers and sonobuoys. Military Mi-4's have been exported to some two dozen air forces in the Soviet bloc and elsewhere, among the largest users being Algeria, Bulgaria, China, Cuba, India, Iraq and Poland.

From 1964 two civil versions of the Mi-4 were also built in considerable numbers. There were the Mi-4P (*Passajarski* = passenger) and the Mi-4S (*Selskokhoziaistvenuii* = rural economy). The Mi-4P is the standard version for Aeroflot, carrying 11 passengers normally or up to 16 in high density seating or,

in the ambulance role, 8 stretchers and a medical attendant. The Mi-4P is distinguished by having square cabin windows, wheel spats and no ventral fairing; 100 kg (220 lb) of baggage can be carried in addition to the normal passenger complement. The Mi-4S is normally used for agricultural operations, when it can be fitted with a 1,000 kg (2,204 lb) dust hopper or a 1,600 litre (352 Imp gal) tank holding pesticide or fire-fighting chemical. All versions of the Mi-4 have provision for fitting inflatable pontoons in addition to the wheeled landing gear. A stripped-down Mi-4 established a number of speed-with-payload and payload-to-altitude records in 1956, and in more recent years both military and civil Mi-4's have performed a considerable amount of useful work in the Polar regions, their tasks including ice patrol and geological survey.

32 Sikorsky S-55 (H-19) and Westland Whirlwind

The second Sikorsky helicopter to be built on a large scale, the S-55 remained in steady production for more than a decade, during which time the parent company built one thousand two hundred and eighty-one, Westland more than four hundred, Mitsubishi forty-four and the SNCA du Sud-Est a further quantity. It was supplied to civil and military customers in nearly thirty countries and today is still a familiar sight in places all over the world.

The first S-55's were five YH-19's completed in 1949–50 for evaluation by the US Air Force. The first of these (49–2012), which made its maiden flight on 10 November 1949, was characterised by a blunt-ended cabin whose rear wall was perpendicular to the tailboom; but the second aircraft and all subsequent S-55's had the angle filled by the triangular fillet that is one of the aircraft's chief recognition features. Production for the US armed forces included fifty H-19A's for the Air Force, seventy-two H-19C Chickasaws for the Army, and ten HO4S-1's for the Navy, all with 600 hp Pratt & Whitney R-1340-57 engines. A version with 700 hp Wright R-1300-3 engine, larger diameter main rotor and a characteristic downward angle to the tailboom was produced in greater numbers, the Air Force receiving two hundred and seventy as H-19B's and SH-19B's, the Army three hundred and thirty-eight as H-19D Chickasaws, and the Navy sixty-one as HO4S-3's. Thirty of the HO4S-3's were built as HO4S-3G rescue models for use by the US Coast Guard; the Marine Corps received sixty HRS-1's, ninety-one HRS-2's and eighty-four HRS-3's, corresponding generally to the HO4S series and used as troop transports. Model redesignations in 1962 included the H-19B (now UH-19B), SH-19B (to HH-19B), H-19C (UH-19C), H-19D (UH-19D), HRS-3 (CH-19E), HO4S-3 (UH-19F), and HO4S-3G (HH-19G). American civil certification for the S-55 was obtained on 25 March 1952, the R-1340-engined model being known as the S-55A, that with the R-1300 being the S-55B and the angled-tailboom version the S-55C.

The Royal Navy received ten Sikorsky-built HRS-2's and fifteen HO4S-3's for rescue and anti-submarine duties respectively as the HAR Mk 21 and HAS Mk 22. Then, following the import of another S-55 as a trials and demonstration aircraft, Westland production began with ten R-1340-40-engined WS-55's as Navy Whirlwind HAR Mk 1's and ten similar HAR Mk 2's for the RAF and Army, the latter for rescue as well as transport duties. The first Westland-built aircraft was flown on 12 November 1952. Two other Westland models were built with American engines: the HAR Mk 3, similar to the HO4S-3, and the HAR Mk 4 with the R-1340-57, used in Malaya in 1954. The US-engined WS-55's, civil as well as military, are known collectively as Whirlwind Series 1's; the Series 2's were fitted with a British power-plant, the 750 hp (derated) Alvis Leonides Major, and the first of these, an HAR Mk 5 for the Royal Navy, was flown on 28 August 1955. The Mk 5 entered Royal Navy service in January 1958, at about the same time as the anti-submarine HAS Mk 7 (first flight 17 October 1956) designed to replace the Gannet. The Mk 7 carries additional personnel to man the radar and dipping Asdic equipment, and has a homing torpedo in a ventral weapons bay. Final piston-engined Westland variant was the HCC Mk 8, two of which were built with 4/7-seat VIP interiors for service with The Queen's Flight. Westland-built Whirlwinds were exported to France (thirty-seven similar to HAR Mk 2) and Yugoslavia (four similar to HAR Mk 5, two similar to HAS Mk 7, and twelve others of these two types – eight Mk 5's and four Mk 7's – in sub-assembly form or without engines). The Gnome turbine-engined Whirlwind Series 3 is described separately, and many piston-engined Whirlwinds have been converted to this form of powerplant.

The S-55/Whirlwind can accommodate up to 8 people in its commercial form or 10 for military purposes; or 6 casualty litters and a medical attendant when used as an ambulance.

33 Sikorsky S-56/HR2S/H-37 Mojave

The Sikorsky S-56 came into being as an assault transport for the US Marine Corps, although some 60 per cent of those eventually built were to meet US Army orders. The original requirement was for an assault transport helicopter capable of air-lifting 26 troops or an equivalent weight of military equipment. The S-56 was Sikorsky's first twin-engined helicopter, although the traditional single main rotor layout was retained. For many years the S-56 was the western world's largest and fastest military helicopter, and held two height-with-payload records from 1956–59. It was also the first production helicopter to have a retractable main undercarriage. Loading of the aircraft was via clamshell nose doors, giving access beneath the flight deck to the 1,900 cu ft (53·80 cu m) cabin. A winch capable of hoisting 2,000 lb (907 kg) at a time was fitted in the cabin roof to assist the loading of cargo.

The US Navy placed an order in May 1951 for a prototype XHR2S-1, which was flown for the first time on 18 December 1953. Three more XHR2S-1's followed, and the first of fifty-five production HR2S-1's was flown on 25 October 1955, deliveries to Marine Corps Squadron HMX-1 starting in July 1956. Two aircraft were modified as HR2S-1W patrol aircraft with a huge AN/APS-20E search radar under the nose and additional crew members for radar picket duties. In 1954 an HR2S-1, redesignated YH-37, was evaluated by the US Army, from which followed orders for ninety-four similar aircraft as H-37A Mojaves for general transport duties. Delivery of the last S-56 was made in May 1960, but Sikorsky was engaged until the end of 1962 in converting all but four of the H-37A's to H-37B (later CH-37B) standard. Improvements in this version included the installation of Lear autostabilisation equipment and the ability to load and unload while the helicopter was hovering. The Navy and Marine S-56's became CH-37C's under the 1962 designation system. Some later production S-56's had 2,100 hp R-2800-54 engines.

The S-56's rotor and transmission systems were utilised in the development of the abortive Westland

Westminster and Sikorsky's own S-60 and S-64 crane helicopters, but hopes of selling the S-56 on the commercial market were not realised, due mainly to the high operating costs of a piston-engined machine of this size. A proposal to fit Lycoming T55 turboshaft engines was not adopted.

34 Westland Whirlwind Series 3

The Whirlwind Series 3 is the Westland-developed version of the WS-55 with gas turbine power, which appeared after Westland had successfully evolved a similar conversion of the Sikorsky S-58 as the Westland Wessex. The first attempt at a Whirlwind conversion of this kind related to the proposed Whirlwind 6 for the RAF, which was to have had a Blackburn Twin Turmo as powerplant. This project was never completed, but in 1958 the second Whirlwind 5, XJ398, was re-engined with an imported General Electric T58 turboshaft to become the prototypes Series 3 Whirlwind. It made its first flight in the new form on 28 February 1959, the lengthened nose where the engine was housed being the only notable external difference from the piston-engined Whirlwind. A Gnome engine, licence-built version of the T58, was installed in the following September, and after further trials with the British engine a substantial order for Gnome-engined Whirlwind HAR Mk 10's for the RAF was announced in April 1960. These comprised an initial batch of

newly-built machines, after whose entry into service existing piston-engined Whirlwinds were returned to be re-engined with Gnomes. Similar conversion of the Royal Navy's Whirlwind 7's produced the HAR Mk 9. The military Series 3's are chiefly employed as general transports, ambulances or rescue aircraft. Accommodation provides for the carriage of 10 troops, 6 casualty litters or a 2,000 lb (907 kg) internal or slung cargo load. The Gnome Whirlwind can also carry a light armament, consisting of four AS.11 or Vigilant anti-tank missiles or two 0·303 in Browning machine-guns. Whirlwind HAR Mk 10's first entered service with No 225 Squadron RAF and were subsequently allocated to Nos 110 and 230 Squadrons. Domestic operators of the commercial Series 3 include Bristow Helicopters Ltd, with eighteen; two with VIP interiors serve with The Queen's Flight as HCC Mk 12's. Export models have been supplied to the Ghana Air Force (three), the Brazilian Navy (eight), the Sultan of Brunei (three), the Nigerian Air Force (one) and the government of Qatar (two). Production of the Series 3 Whirlwind was phased out in the spring of 1968.

35 Sikorsky S-58/H-34 Choctaw, Seabat and Seahorse

The first prototype of this widely used helicopter was designed to meet a 1952 requirement of the US Navy for a larger and more up-to-date helicopter to replace the S-55 on anti-submarine patrol work. Designated XHSS-1, it flew for the first time on 8 March 1954, since when more than eighteen hundred have been built for service in many parts of the world. The first of two hundred and fifty-eight production HSS-1's flew on 20 September 1954, and deliveries began in August 1955. Later redesignated SH-34G, it was given the name Seabat and carried either dunking sonar search equipment or weapons for attacking submarines. For night operations, one hundred and twenty examples were built of the SH-34J (previously HSS-1N) with automatic stabilisation and other equipment improvements. After their replacement by the SH-3 Sea King, many Seabats were converted to UH-34G and UH-34J utility transports.

The US Marine Corps, by whom the S-58 was known as the Seahorse, has used the type from 1957 primarily for utility transport and miscellaneous duties including the recovery of early US satellites. The 12-passenger UH-34D and UH-34E (formerly HUS-1 and HUS-1A) were basically alike, forty of the latter being built with pontoons for landing on water. The VH-34D (five built) was a VIP transport. In all, three hundred and eighty-four Seahorses were built for the US Marine Corps. Army S-58's have the name Choctaw, the CH-34A and CH-34C differing only in the equipment carried, and entering service in April 1955 as 16-seat transports or crane helicopters. Substantial numbers of military S-58 variants were exported, and by mid-1972

were serving with the Federal German Army (ninety) and Chinese Nationalist Army (seven); the navies of Brazil (five), France (thirty), Germany (twenty-five), Italy (nine), the Netherlands (six) and Uruguay (one); and the air forces of Belgium (eight), Khmer (two), Laos (four), the Philippines (two) and Thailand (twenty). One hundred and thirty-five were assembled in France by Sud-Aviation, which subsequently manufactured one hundred and sixty-six more under licence.

The commercial S-58B and S-58D are passenger/cargo transport helicopters comparable with their military counterparts. The 12-seat airline version, certificated by the FAA in August 1956, was built for Chicago Helicopter Airways (eight), New York Airways (three) and Sabena (eight). Production of the S-58 ended in December 1965 after one thousand seven hundred and sixty-six had been built by Sikorsky, but was later started again to fulfil additional requirements under the US Military Assistance Program. These were completed by January 1970, at which time Sikorsky's production total had risen to one thousand eight hundred and twenty-one. At this time Sikorsky first announced plans, which were put into effect a year later, to produce and market kits whereby the S-58 can be converted to twin-turbine configuration by installing an 1,800 shp Pratt & Whitney (UACL) PT6 Turbo Twin Pac powerplant. With this installation the aircraft is designated S-58T.

The turbine-engined S-58 development produced by Westland as the Wessex is described separately.

36 Westland Wessex

After acquiring a licence in 1956 to manufacture the Sikorsky S-58 helicopter, Westland imported one of these aircraft in HSS-1 configuration. Given the British serial number XL722, this aircraft was test-flown for a time with its original 1,525 hp Wright R-1820-84 engine before being modified to accept a 1,100 shp Napier Gazelle NGa.11 turboshaft. In its new form it was flown for the first time on 17 May 1957, and was later joined by two pre-production Wessex HAS Mk 1's for naval trials; the first of these flew on 20 June 1958. The HAS Mk 1 (crew of 4) went into production in 1959 for the Royal Navy as a submarine search and strike helicopter equipped with dipping sonar and provision for one or two homing torpedoes. Powered by a 1,450 shp Gazelle Mk 161 engine, it began service trials with No 700H Flight in April 1960 and was subsequently delivered to Nos 706, 737, 771, 815, 819 and 848 Squadrons. The first of these to commission, in July 1961, was No 815; the Wessexes of No 848 Squadron were for commando assault duties aboard HMS *Albion*, having the ASW gear removed to make room for 16 troops or 8 stretchers and a medical attendant in the main cabin. Alternatively, a slung load of 4,000 lb (1,814 kg) can be suspended from an under-fuselage hook. From January 1967 the Wessex Mk 1's were joined in service by the HAS Mk 3,

which is powered by a 1,600 shp Gazelle Mk 165 and has an extended rotor head fairing and large dorsal radome. Twenty-seven HAS Mk 31's supplied to the Royal Australian Navy from August 1962 are similar to the HAS Mk 1 apart from their 1,540 shp Gazelle Mk 162 engines.

All other Wessex variants that were built have two coupled Gnome engines in place of the single Gazelle. These include the RAF's HC Mk 2, flown for the first time in production form on 5 October 1962 and entering service with No 38 Group in February 1964; the Navy's HU Mk 5 (first flight 31 May 1963), which entered service in summer 1964 as a commando-carrier assault transport; twelve Mk 52's for the Iraqi Air Force, three Mk 53's for the Ghana Air Force, and one Mk 54 for the Brunei government. Two Mk 2's were converted to HCC Mk 4 VIP transports for service with The Queen's Flight. Eighteen Wessex Mk 60's were built for Bristow Helicopters Ltd. These are 10-passenger commercial equivalents of the Mk 2 and were used initially in support of oil and gas drilling rigs in the North Sea.

37 & 38 Bell Models 204 and 205 (UH-1) Iroquois

Since June 1955, when it won a US Army competition for a new utility, casualty evacuation and training helicopter, the Bell 204 and its descendants have been in continuous production. Total orders to date have amounted to many thousands (including more than six thousand Model 205's), and the latest versions have double the power and carrying capacity of the original prototypes. These were three XH-40 test aircraft, ordered in 1955 and each powered by a 700 shp Lycoming T53 engine; the first XH-40 (55-4459) was flown on 22 October 1956. Six YH-40's then followed for service trials, these having longer cabins and landing skids and 770 shp engines. From June 1959 the US Army began to receive the first of nine pre-production HU-1's for field tests, which were followed by seventy-four of the initial production version, the HU-1A. The 'HU' designation (inverted to UH in 1962) gave rise to the nickname 'Huey' which is more often used than the aircraft's official name of Iroquois. The HU-1A was followed by four YHU-1B's with 960 shp T53-L-5 engines, redesigned rotor blades and an enlarged cabin seating 2 crew members and 7 passengers or 3 stretchers. Total production orders for HU-1B's subsequently exceeded seven hundred aircraft, the 1,100 shp T53-L-11 engine being fitted in the later batches. In the late autumn of 1962 armed HU-1B's (and some of the HU-1A's) became operational with the US forces in Vietnam, the HU-1B being equipped with four 7·62 mm M-60 machine-guns and two pods of air-to-ground unguided rockets. The HU-1B was superseded in 1965 by the faster and more manoeuvrable UH-1C, which has a new Bell-developed 'door-hinge' rotor and a T53-L-11 engine.

The UH-1C was preceded into service (in May 1963) by the UH-1D, easily the most numerous version with more than a thousand being built. The UH-1D has the Bell Model number 205 and features a much-enlarged cabin accommodating 12–14 troops or 6 casualty litters and a medical attendant in addition to the crew. Production examples were preceded by seven YHU-1D's, the first of which flew on 16 August 1961; powerplant is the T53-L-11. The UH-1D became the workhorse helicopter of the Vietnam campaign, where it has been used for a wide variety of roles including trooping and armed patrol or escort. It has been ordered by the air forces of many countries, and three hundred and fifty-two were ordered by the Federal German forces, these being built in Germany with Dornier the principal contractor.

The UH-1E broadly resembles the UH-1B and C, but has special equipment including a rescue hoist and was built for the US Marine Corps as an assault transport helicopter with two M-60 gun pods and up to thirty-six 2·75 in HVAR rockets. Delivery began in February 1964. The US Air Force ordered one hundred and forty-six examples of the UH-1F, with 1,100 shp (derated) T58-GE-3 engines, for missile site support duties, together with a number of TH-1F trainer versions; first flight of a UH-1F was made on 20 February 1964, and delivery began in September 1964. No G model was announced, the next model being the UH-1H, six hundred and nineteen being ordered for the US Army, thirty for the USAF, thirteen for the RNZAF, and ten CUH-1H for the Canadian Armed Forces. The UH-1H replaces the UH-1D, to which it is identical except for a 1,400 shp T53-L-13 engine. From mid-1966 large numbers of UH-1B's and UH-1D's were refitted with Decca navigation equipment, and lightweight armoured crew seats were built for the aircraft in Vietnam. Later versions of the Model 204 included twenty-seven HH-1K (air/sea rescue), forty-five TH-1L (training) and eight UH-1L (utility) helicopters for the US Navy; and a small batch of night-fighting UH-1M's for US Army evaluation.

Bell produced relatively small quantities of the 204B, commercial and military export counterpart of the UH-1B, which was certificated by the FAA in April 1963. This is a 10-seater with a slightly longer tail-boom than the military version and a larger rotor. Slightly more than sixty commercial 204B's were built; twenty-four others were supplied to the RAAF, and eight to the Royal Australian Navy. Mitsui in Japan holds a sales licence for the 204B/UH-1B, and since spring 1966 has supplied Fuji-built machines to All Nippon Airways (two), Asahi Helicopter Co (two), the Tokyo Metropolitan Police department (one) and the Japan Ground Self-Defence Force (ninety). A further eighty-one UH-1H's are to be built by Fuji up to 1976. The major licensee, however, is Agusta in Italy, which builds the 204B, 205 and 205A-1 for various European and Middle Eastern cus-

tomers. The first Agusta-Bell 204 was flown on 10 May 1961 and had a 1,050 shp Bristol Siddeley Gnome H.1000 engine. A version with the 1,250 shp Gnome H.1200 was flown two years later, and the Gnome or the General Electric T58 are still available in place of the T53-L-11. Agusta-Bell 204/205-series helicopters have been built for all three Italian services; for the armed forces of Austria, Ethiopia, Greece, Iran, Kuwait, Morocco, the Netherlands, Oman, Saudi Arabia, Spain, Sweden, Turkey and Zambia; and for commercial operators in Italy, the Lebanon, Norway, Sweden and Switzerland. Those for the Italian and Spanish navies are equipped for the anti-submarine role, with dipping sonar and a pair of Mk 44 homing torpedoes. Agusta has also developed a specialised anti-submarine version for the Italian Navy, known as the AB 204AS.

A twin-engined development, combining the basic UH-1H airframe with a 1,250 shp PT6T Turbo Twin-Pac engine, is in production as the UH-1N for the USAF (seventy-nine), US Navy (fifty), US Marine Corps (thirty-six) and the Canadian Armed Forces (fifty CUH-1N), and for commercial customers.

39 Agusta A 106

Flown in prototype form in November 1965, the Agusta A 106 is a small lightweight armed helicopter designed initially to fulfil an anti-submarine attack role. Its predecessors were the experimental piston-engined A 103 and A 104, and the A 105 which was flown in

April 1964 with an Agusta-built Astazou turboshaft engine.

The single-seat A 106 is in production (twenty-three ordered) for the Italian Navy. It will serve on board the 'Impavido' class guided missile armed destroyers as an anti-submarine helicopter operable in poor weather and carrying target identification equipment and a pair of underslung Mk 44 homing torpedoes. Provision exists for auxiliary flotation gear in addition to the standard skid landing gear, and an auxiliary fuel tank may be carried externally on each side of the fuselage, aft of the cabin. The 2-blade main rotor, and the tail section including the 2-blade tail rotor, can be folded for stowage on board ship.

Alternative possible applications of the A 106 are Army support; light crane duties with loads suspended from an under-fuselage hook; or casualty evacuation with 2 externally-mounted stretcher cases.

40 Hughes OH-6 Cayuse and Model 500

In 1960 the US Department of Defense issued Technical Specification 153 for an aircraft that was, nominally, in the LOH (Light Observation Helicopter) category. What it really wanted was a single new helicopter capable of performing a variety of duties which had hitherto required the deployment of three or four different types of aircraft: such duties as personnel or cargo transport, light ground attack or casualty evacuation, in addition to those of observation and photo-graphic reconnaissance. Twelve US manufacturers submitted over a score of proposed designs, and from these were selected one each from Bell, Hiller and Hughes. Five prototypes of each design were ordered in spring 1961 for comparative tests; the Bell HO-4 was then eliminated from the contest, leaving the choice to be made between the Hiller HO-5 and the Hughes HO-6.

The Hughes entry, evolved under the design leadership of M. S. Harned, carried the manufacturer's Model number 369 and was given the revised military designation OH-6A in July 1962. On 27 February 1963 the first OH-6A (N9696F) made its maiden flight, and US Army trials began at Fort Rucker, Alabama, in the following November. Selection of the OH-6A for production was announced in May 1965. One thousand four hundred and thirty-four OH-6A's were ordered, delivery of which started in September 1966 and was due for completion by August 1970. Within an airframe that is dimensionally not much bigger than the Hughes 200 (q.v.), the Cayuse packs a large amount of technical ingenuity and operational versatility. The key to this is the very small and light Allison T63-A-5A engine, driving a fully-articulated 4-blade main rotor, whose blades are of similar pattern to those on the Hughes 200. The OH-6A can carry 2 pilots and 4 fully-equipped troops. 'Kit' type ordnance, which may be attached to the cabin on the port side, includes an XM-75 grenade launcher or an XM-27 machine-gun pod. The latter can be pivoted through 90 degrees to fire forward or at intermediate downward angles.

In addition to the five US Army prototypes, Hughes built four others for its own purposes, and from one of these completed in 1966 a mock-up of a proposed civil executive version of the OH-6A, the Model 500. A true prototype Model 500, N9000F, was flown for the first time in early 1967. This is powered by the civil version of the T63 engine, currently derated to 278 shp, and seats up to 5 people including the pilot(s). Basic FAA certification of the OH-6A also covers the Model 500.

The 500C is an alternative commercial version with a 400 shp engine for improved 'hot and high' performance. A military export version, designated 500M, has been ordered by the armed forces of Argentina (twenty-six), Bolivia (twelve), Colombia (twelve), Denmark (twelve), Dominica (seven), Japan (GSDF one hundred and sixty-five, MSDF twelve), Nicaragua (four), Spain (five) and Taiwan (six).

No fewer than 23 international records were set up by OH-6A helicopters in March and April 1966, including one for a distance of 2,213 miles (3,561·55 km) in a straight line and another for a speed of 171·81 mph (276·506 km/hr) over a closed circuit. One OH-6A (12968), with a 5-blade main rotor and 'blanketed' engine installation, is claimed to be the world's quietest helicopter to date, and another aircraft has been similarly modified under the designation OH-6C.

41 Westland/Aérospatiale Lynx

Third to fly of the trio of helicopters covered by the 1967 Anglo-French agreement, the Lynx was known originally as the W.G.13 and is the only one of the three types in which the UK company has design leadership. The illustration shows the first of five prototypes, which was flown for the first time on 21 March 1971. A further seven Lynxes, intended for the main military development programme, were in course of construction in mid-1972, by which time all of the original five had been completed. Initial production will be focused upon the general-purpose AH Mk 1 for the British Army, and the HAS Mk 2 anti-submarine search and strike version for the Royal Navy and the French and Argentine navies. Prototypes of these versions made their first flights on 12 April 1972 (XX153) and 25 May 1972 (XX469) respectively. Future development is planned to include a trainer version for the RAF and models for the civil market. On 20 June 1972, XX153 set up a new world class speed record, over a 15–25 km course, of 200 mph (321·87 km/hr); two days later, over a 100 km closed circuit, the same aircraft achieved an average speed of 197·9 mph (318·5 km/hr).

The general-purpose version carries a crew of 1 or 2 pilots, with cabin accommodation for up to 10 troops; 3 stretchers, 2 sitting casualties and a medical attendant; or up to 2,000 lb (907 kg) of cargo. Instead of an internal load, it can carry up to 2,200 lb (1,000 kg) externally on an underfloor cargo hook. Optional equipment for other roles includes a 600 lb (272 kg) capacity rescue hoist, flotation gear, various in-the-cabin gun installations, or external racks on the cabin sides for gun and rocket pods or AS.11, AS.12 or Swingfire air-to-surface missiles. The naval version has a tricycle wheeled landing gear, with provision also for flotation gear and a harpoon deck-mooring system. Its internally-stowed ASW equipment is classified, but other items include Ferranti Seaspray surface search radar, retractable target detection and classification gear and two Mk 44 homing torpedoes or alternative weapons. Among the latter, specific mention has been made of the BAC CL384, a homing missile currently under development for attacking light surface craft. Alternative roles for the naval version include passenger or supply transport, air/sea search and rescue, and carrier plane-guard duties. In April 1972 Sikorsky in the US began flight testing the Sea Lynx, a version which it is to enter as its candidate in the US Navy's LAMPS competition for a new anti-submarine and anti-ship missile defence helicopter.

42 Bell Model 206 JetRanger/OH-58 Kiowa

Both of the losing finalists in the US Army's Light Observation Helicopter competition later re-emerged as contenders in the civil market. The first to be eliminated was Bell's OH-4A, whose first prototype (N7399) flew on 8 December 1962. Unlike Fairchild Hiller, which produced prototype FH-1100's by con-

verting existing OH-5A's, Bell utilised its five OH-4A's for general research work and built a completely new prototype (N8590F) as the Model 206A. This was flown for the first time at Fort Worth on 10 January 1966 and was soon joined by two more aircraft to speed FAA certification, which was awarded on 20 October 1966. The JetRanger retains the engine and rotor system of its military ancestor, uses the full available power of its Allison engine and has a 5-seat cabin of entirely new design. The JetRanger first entered production, by Bell in the United States and Agusta in Italy, to meet commercial orders from customers in the USA, Canada, Australia, Britain and continental Europe, and was then offered in executive, utility or cargo form.

Subsequently the US Army re-opened its LOH competition, of which the JetRanger was declared the winner in March 1968. To date (1972) a total of two thousand two hundred have been ordered for the US Army, delivery of which began in May 1969. These aircraft are known as the OH-58A Kiowa; they have a 35 ft 4 in (10·77 m) diameter main rotor and minor internal differences from the commercial JetRanger. The US Navy has forty dual-control TH-57A SeaRangers for primary training. Bell has also received orders for military Jet-Rangers from Canada (seventy-four COH-58A) and the Australian Army (seventy-five); only twelve of the latter are being built by Bell, the remainder being assembled in Australia by Commonwealth Aircraft

Corporation. Seven JetRangers (four of them armed) have been supplied to the Brazilian Air Force, which designates them OH-4. Bell's Australian deal also includes the sale of one hundred and sixteen commercial JetRangers.

In spring 1971 Bell introduced the Model 206B JetRanger II, which has improved performance resulting from the installation of a 400 shp Allison 250-C20 turboshaft engine, and earlier JetRangers can be modified to this standard. Production by Agusta of both versions was continuing in 1972, the Italian licensee by then having built more than four hundred civil and military JetRangers. Customers for Agusta-Bell JetRangers have included the armed forces of Iran, Italy, Saudi Arabia, Spain, Sweden and Turkey.

43 Bell Model 209 (AH-1) HueyCobra and SeaCobra

The Bell Model 209 HueyCobra came into being as a result of a crash programme initiated by the US Army when the campaign in Vietnam revealed the need for a fast, well-armed aircraft to provide escort and fire support for the CH-47A Chinook.

Bell had already investigated the potential of an armed support helicopter with the OH-13X Sioux Scout, a tandem-seat derivative of the Model 47 flown in September 1963 with a 260 hp Lycoming TVO-435 engine. A development along similar lines of the UH-1 Iroquois was, therefore, the logical follow-on to this approach, and this was proposed and accepted by the US Army in 1965. A prototype of the new aircraft (N209J) was flown for the first time on 7 September 1965, having the same rotor and transmission systems and the same T53-L-13 engine as the UH-1C Iroquois. The entirely new fuselage has a low silhouette and extremely narrow frontal area (3 ft 2 in = 0·965 m at its widest point) which renders the HueyCobra easy to conceal on the ground and a much less easy target in the air than a conventional helicopter. In December 1965, N209J arrived at Edwards Air Force Base for service trials, and two pre-series AH-1G's were ordered on 4 April 1966. Nine days later came an order for one hundred and ten production aircraft, a total that had risen to eight hundred and thirty-eight by the end of 1968. A further two hundred and forty were added subsequently, and production of these was nearing completion in 1972. Delivery of production Huey-Cobras to the US Army began in June 1967, the type becoming operational in Vietnam in the early autumn. Thirty-eight of the above AH-1G's were allocated to the US Marine Corps in 1969, in advance of the delivery of its own order for AH-1J SeaCobras (see below). The AH-1G has also been ordered by the RAAF (eleven) and Spanish Navy (four).

On a typical mission the AH-1G can reach its target in about half the time taken by the Iroquois, can remain in the combat zone much longer and can wield twice the fire-power. The first production machines had an Emerson TAT-102A (Tactical Assault Turret) under the nose, in which is mounted a 7·62 mm six-barrelled General Electric GAU2B/A Minigun, operated by the co-pilot/gunner from the front seat. Later-production aircraft have an XM-28 armament system incorporating either two Miniguns, two 40 mm grenade launchers, or one of each. The stub wings have four attachment points for stores which are fired by the pilot. Initially these points carried XM-159 pods each containing nineteen 2·75 in rockets, but other loads may comprise XM-157 pods with seven rockets each, two XM-18 Minigun pods, or an XM-35 20 mm gun kit. The airframe is capable of being fitted, alternatively, with a turret capable of firing one M-61 Vulcan multi-barrel 20 mm gun, an XM-197 three-barrel 20 mm gun, or a three-barrel 30 mm gun. The crew seats and cabin sides are armour-protected.

A twin-turbine version of the HueyCobra, powered by a 1,250 shp UACL T400-CP-400 Turbo Twin Pac engine, is in production for the US Marine Corps as the AH-1J SeaCobra. An initial quantity of forty-nine AH-1J's was ordered in May 1968, and delivery of these began in mid-1970. The AH-1J is dimensionally almost identical to the AH-1G, and carries a substantially similar armament. A further development, the Bell Model 309 KingCobra, is described separately.

44 Sikorsky S-67 Blackhawk
Originating under the Sikorsky pro-ject designation AH-3, the S-67 Blackhawk was designed in 1969 as a 'tank killer' gunship helicopter, and a company-funded prototype (N671SA) flew for the first time on 20 August 1970. Incorporated in the design are proven dynamic components based on those of the S-61R, and a number of features of Sikorsky's earlier S-66 design, which was evolved for the US Army's AAFSS (Advanced Aerial Fire Support System) competition of 1965. Added to these, in an airframe having the typical low drag, low frontal area profile demanded of the contemporary gunship helicopter, are a number of other features which are new to this class of aeroplane. They include an all-moving tailplane, which is set in a vertical attitude for hovering and can be used in the conventional position during horizontal flight to trim the fuselage independently of the main rotor – a useful factor in aligning a gunship to concentrate fire upon a target. The Blackhawk has 5-blade main and tail rotors, the former having swept-back blade tips. Much of the work of the anti-torque tail rotor can be undertaken by the cambered vertical fin, and indeed the S-67 can be flown and landed safely even if the tail rotor is shot away. The landing gear consists of twin retractable pairs of main wheels and a tailwheel, the S-67 being unusual in that it touches down on the tailwheel first. The outer stub-wings, which are detachable, have (for the first time in a helicopter) speed brakes on both upper and lower surfaces. These improve several aspects of perform-

ance, including manoeuvrability, diving angle and time on target. The wings have four attachment points for external weapons, and can carry 16 TOW, Swingfire, HOT or similar missiles, thirty-two 5 in Zuni rockets or 8 launchers containing a total of one hundred and fifty-two 2·75 in folding-fin rockets. Beneath the fuselage (and, optionally, the nose) can be fitted turrets for 7·62 mm Miniguns, 20 and 30 mm cannon or a 40 mm grenade launcher. The Blackhawk carries a 2-man crew for the anti-tank role, and a fuselage compartment permits the transport of 6 fully-armed troops. In unarmed configuration this compartment can be enlarged to seat up to 15 troops. Alternative applications for the Blackhawk include long range rescue, with two 300 US gallon (1,136 litre) underwing drop-tanks; anti-submarine warfare; or as a flying crane, carrying up to 7,000 lb (3,175 kg) of externally-slung cargo with the wings removed. Up to autumn 1972 no further examples of the S-67 had flown. The prototype set a helicopter world speed record on 14 December 1970, beating it five days later with a new record of 220·885 mph (355·485 km/hr). Although larger than other contemporary gunship designs, the Blackhawk is highly manoeuvrable, and can be rolled and perform split-S turns without difficulty. In the late summer of 1972 the Blackhawk, Bell KingCobra and Lockheed Cheyenne (which see) took part in a US Army fly-off competition, from which the Cheyenne was eliminated. The

future of the other two participants had not been decided at the time of closing for press.

45 Bell Model 309 KingCobra

The KingCobra, as its name suggests, is basically a further development of the HueyCobra/SeaCobra family of helicopter gunships already in wide-scale service with the US Army and Marine Corps. It is, in effect, a slightly stretched version of the latter's AH-1J SeaCobra, having a 4 ft 7 in (1·40 m) longer fuselage and a 4 ft 0 in (1·22 m) greater diameter main rotor. Wider-chord blades are fitted to both the main and tail rotors, and the former have double-swept tips to reduce the noise level and improve their high-speed performance. Two prototypes of the KingCobra have been built. The first of these (N309J) was flown on 10 September 1971, and first details of the aircraft were announced later the same month. The King-Cobra was developed primarily with existing AH-1 customers in mind; hence the first prototype satisfies the USMC's preference for a twin-engined configuration in having an 1,800 shp UACL T400-CP-400 Turbo Twin Pac powerplant, while the second prototype (first flown in January 1972) has a single 2,050 shp Lycoming T55-L-7C turboshaft engine. Other modifications, compared with the Sea-Cobra, include an increase in wing span from 10 ft 4 in (3·15 m) to 13 ft 0 in (3·96 m), permitting increases in internal fuel load and external stores-carrying capability; strengthened airframe and landing gear, to absorb the greater engine power; and the addition of a ventral fin to improve directional stability and control. The KingCobra has four underwing stores points, on which a typical load would be 8 Hughes TOW missiles and 2 pods each containing nineteen 2·75 in folding-fin rockets. The 'chin' turret can mount a multi-barrel 30 mm or 20 mm gun, and modifications to the nose area include the installation of FLIR (forward-looking infra-red) sensors, a laser rangefinder, low light level television and an enlarged ammunition bay. Due to its lighter weight and smaller weapons load than the Blackhawk, Bell claims that the KingCobra can be produced at much lower cost than either of its original competitors, since existing 'Cobra production assemblies can be utilised with minimal modification. With the Sikorsky Blackhawk (which see), the King-Cobra took part in an initial US Army flight test competition in 1972, but its future remained undecided at the time of closing for press.

46 **Lockheed AH-56A Cheyenne**
Lockheed began its study of modern rotorcraft techniques in 1958, a comparatively late entry into this field of aircraft design. The rigid-rotor principle, as used in the Cheyenne, has only been achieved in practical form in comparatively recent times.

Lockheed first tested the basic soundness of its rigid-rotor concept in the CL-475 prototype (N6940C) in late 1959, and from this designed the larger 2-seat CL-595, three of

which were built. One of these, designated XH-51N, was delivered to NASA for wind tunnel tests; the other two, designated XH-51A (serial numbers 151262 and '63), were evaluated by the US Army and Navy. First XH-51A to fly was 151262, which made its maiden flight on 2 November 1962, powered by a 500 shp Pratt & Whitney T74 turboshaft engine. Later, one was converted into a compound helicopter, with a 2,600 lb (1,180 kg) st J60-P-2 turbojet on the port side of the fuselage and a pair of stub wings to off-load the rotor during forward flight. In May 1965 this aeroplane flew faster than any previous rotorcraft, achieving a level speed of 272 mph (438 km/hr).

The AH-56 Cheyenne is also a turbine-powered compound helicopter using a rigid-rotor system for lift and a pusher propeller at the rear for forward propulsion. During forward flight nearly 90 per cent of the Cheyenne's engine power is diverted to the tail propeller. More than a dozen US manufacturers competed with Lockheed for the original AAFSS (Advanced Aerial Fire Support System) contract, from which a choice between projects from Lockheed and Sikorsky was resolved in March 1966, when Lockheed received a contract for ten development aircraft. The first of these, for dynamic tests, was rolled out in May 1967, the first flying prototype (66-1127) took to the air on 21 September 1967, and two more development aircraft were delivered later. The remaining six were 'frozen' in a partially-completed condition. In January 1968 the US Army took up an option to buy three hundred and seventy-five Cheyennes, which were scheduled to enter service in the early 1970s as armed escorts for larger support helicopters and as ground attack aircraft. This contract was, however, cancelled in spring 1969, although development of the Cheyenne continued. In 1972 it was involved in a fly-off competition, for a new Army requirement, with the Sikorsky Blackhawk and Bell King-Cobra (which see). The Cheyenne was eliminated as a result of this competition, and its future remained undecided at the time of closing for press, although Lockheed is to continue developing the advanced rigid-rotor control system.

The crew are seated in tandem, the co-pilot/gunner occupying the front seat and controlling the nose turret, which mounts either a 7·62 mm Minigun or a 40 mm grenade launcher, and can be traversed through 180 degrees. A 30 mm cannon with a full 360-degree field of fire is mounted in a barbette below the rear fuselage. Two strong-points beneath each wing are stressed to take Hughes TOW (Tube-launched, Optically-tracked, Wire-guided) anti-tank missiles or pods of 2·75 in (70 mm) rockets. Computer sighting is installed for weapon firing.

47–50 & 68 Sikorsky S-61 (military variants)

By early 1972 more than seven hundred military and civil examples of the S-61 twin-turbine helicopter had been delivered, and the type

has been in service in various roles since 1961. It was ordered to meet a 1957 US Navy requirement for a submarine hunter/killer aircraft, and in prototype form was known as the XHSS-2, making its maiden flight on 11 March 1959. Service trials were conducted in 1960 with seven YHSS-2's, the production HSS-2 (now SH-3A) Sea King being delivered to US Navy Squadrons from September 1961. This model carries dunking sonar submarine search gear and homing torpedoes, and is powered by T58-GE-8B engines; manufacturer's designation is S-61B. Nine SH-3A's were converted to RH-3A for mine countermeasures work, and three others are used by the US Air Force for missile site support and drone recovery. Three SH-3A's were supplied in 1963 to Japan, where Mitsubishi is completing a further eighty for the Japan Maritime Self-Defence Force, and United Aircraft Corporation in Canada completed all except four of the forty-one CHSS-2's ordered by the Royal Canadian Navy. Eight similar VH-3A's, with 12-passenger VIP interiors, serve as special transports with the US Army (two) and Marine Corps (six). A version generally similar to the SH-3A for transport or rescue duties is the S-61A; nine serve with No 722 Squadron of the Royal Danish Air Force in the air/sea rescue role. Three, designated CH-3B, are operated by the USAF on missile site support and drone recovery; and in 1967 ten 31-seat troop/cargo transport S-61A-4's began to be delivered to the Royal Malaysian Air Force, by whom the type is known as the Nuri. A further six were delivered to the RMAF from August 1971.

From 1966 the SH-3A was superseded in production by the SH-3D, with 1,400 shp T58-GE-10 engines. Six SH-3D's have been supplied to the Spanish Navy, and four to the Brazilian Navy; Agusta has built twenty-four for the Italian Navy, has additional orders for the Italian armed forces, and is building ten for the Imperial Iranian Navy; and Westland is producing for the Royal Navy and other customers a variant with more advanced British electronics and 1,500 shp Gnome H.1400 turbines. The first production Westland-built Sea King (XV642, an HAS Mk 1 for the Royal Navy), was flown on 7 May 1969. By late 1972 total Westland orders had reached one hundred and ten, including ASW Sea Kings for the Indian Navy (nine Mk 42) and Royal Australian Navy (ten Mk 50) and SAR (search and rescue) models for the Federal German Navy (twenty-two Mk 41) and Norwegian Air Force (ten Mk 43). In 1971 Sikorsky began converting more than twenty SH-3A's into utility SH-3G's by removing the ASW equipment and (in six aircraft) installing an armament of Minigun pods. In the second half of 1971 some SH-3G's (eleven initially) were further converted to become multi-purpose SH-3H's, with new ASW equipment and T58-GE-10 engines, and these entered service in mid-1972.

The other major military version is the S-61R, first flown as the civil prototype N664Y on 17 June 1963 and nicknamed 'Jolly Green Giant' by the USAF. This is a heavy transport helicopter using the same powerplant and rotor system as the SH-3A but having a bigger, re-designed fuselage with 'kneeling' undercarriage, a rear-loading ramp and other changes. One hundred and thirty-three were ordered by the US Air Force as CH-3C's or HH-3E's with 1,300 shp T58-GE-1 engines, but from February 1966 the 1,500 shp T58-GE-5 was installed. With the latter engine the aircraft is known as the CH-3E, and all CH-3C's were due to be brought up to CH-3E or HH-3E standard. The CH-3E can carry up to 30 troops, 15 stretchers or a 5,000 lb (2,268 kg) load of vehicles or other military equipment; an Emerson Electric TAT-102 turret may be fitted in the leading edge of each sponson. The HH-3E's of the USAF's Aerospace Rescue and Recovery Service are generally similar to the CH-3E, but have protective armour, a defensive armament, rescue hoist and telescopic flight refuelling probe. Two of these aircraft left New York on 31 May 1967 for the Salon de l'Aéronautique at Le Bourget, where they arrived the following day after the first-ever non-stop helicopter crossing of the North Atlantic. Nine in-flight refuellings were made by each aircraft during the 4,270 mile (6,870 km) journey. The first of thirty-four HH-3F's were delivered to the US Coast Guard in 1968, with six more on option. These have a rescue hoist, and a search radome on the nose beneath the port side windscreen, but otherwise resemble the HH-3E except for the deletion of armament, armour and self-sealing fuel tanks.

On 21 May 1965 Sikorsky began flight testing, under a two-year Army/Navy programme, the S-61F compound helicopter, an SH-3A with a new, streamlined fuselage, fully retractable undercarriage, and other airframe improvements including two 3,000 lb (1,360 kg) st Pratt & Whitney J60 podded jet engines. This aircraft reached a level speed of 242 mph (390 km/hr) in this form, and was later fitted with 32 ft 0 in (9·75 m) span wings.

51 Sikorsky S-61L and S-61N

These commercial models of the S-61 helicopter use the same rotor system with a new and longer fuselage. The S-61L is a landplane model, although its hull is sealed against the possibility of making an emergency landing on water, and all undercarriage units are non-retracting. It seats 28 passengers in the standard airline seating layout and carries a flight crew of 3. The S-61N is fully amphibious and can be identified by its twin stabilising floats, into which the main land-wheels can be retracted. Both versions can seat a maximum of 30 passengers. First flights of the L and N versions were made on 6 December 1960 and 7 August 1962 respectively. The S-61L received FAA certification – the first for a twin-turbine commercial helicopter – in November 1961 and since October 1964 both versions have been cleared

for all-weather operation. Current production examples have 1,500 shp CT58-140-2 turboshaft engines. The only customers so far for the S-61L are Los Angeles Airways, which has a fleet of seven and on 1 March 1962 became the first operator to put the commercial S-61 into service; Carson Helicopters (one); and New York Airways (four). Customers up to early 1972 for the S-61N included All Nippon Airways (one); Ansett-ANA (one); BEA Helicopters (seven); Bristow Helicopters (three); Brunei Shell (two); the Canadian Ministry of Transport (one); Court Line Helicopters, South Africa (one); Elivie, Italy (two); Greenlandair (five); Helikopter Service, Norway (four); Japan Air Lines (one); KLM (two); Nitto Airways, Japan (one); Okanagan, Canada (two); and San Francisco & Oakland Helicopter Airlines (four).

52 Sikorsky S-62

The Sikorsky S-62 was the first turbine-powered helicopter to be granted a type approval certificate by the US Federal Aviation Agency. Its design, drawn up in 1957–58, was based on using identical main and tail rotors and transmission systems, and other dynamic and mechanical features, of the thoroughly proven piston-engined S-55. The fuselage was entirely new, being designed for amphibious operation with a flying-boat hull and main undercarriage wheels semi-retractable within the two outrigged stabilising floats. Power is provided by a single General Electric turboshaft engine, mounted centrally above the main cabin, and accommodation provides for a 2-man flight crew and 10 airline passengers or 12 troops.

Two S-62 prototypes were completed, with 1,050 shp T58-GE-6 engines derated to 670 shp. The maiden flight on 22 May 1958, and subsequent world-wide demonstration flights, were made by N880, while N972 carried out trials for the FAA type certificate which was awarded on 30 June 1960; a few days later the first production machine, designated S-62A, was delivered to a commercial customer. Later S-62A's have CT58-100 or -110 engines of 1,250 (derated to 730) shp. In February 1962, after service trials with a modified S-62A, the US Navy ordered four of these aircraft as HU2S-1G's for the US Coast Guard. Subsequent naval orders for the HH-52A, as this version is now known, raised the total to ninety-nine, and it has been in use since early 1963. The HH-52A has the T58-GE-8 engine, military version of the CT58-110, and automatic stabilisation equipment. Additional features for coastal search and rescue work include a fold-down rescue platform and boat-towing gear. A rescue hoist can be mounted above the starboard cabin door to lift a maximum load of 600 lb (272 kg), or the S-62A can lift a 3,000 lb (1,361 kg) slung load by means of an under-fuselage hook.

Two other S-62 variants have also been produced. The S-62B is essentially similar to the A model, but employs the rotor system of the Sikorsky S-58 with the main blades shortened by 1 ft 1 in (0·33 m). The S-62C is the equivalent of the HH-52A for commercial and foreign military customers, and was supplied to the Indian Air Force (two), Japan Air and Maritime Self-Defence Forces (nine each), Philippine Air Force (two) and Royal Thai Police Force (two). The biggest single civil operator of S-62's is Petroleum Helicopters Inc, which has a fleet of six for work in support of offshore oil-drilling operations in the Gulf of Mexico. Of the S-62 helicopters ordered, other than those of the USCG, twenty-six were built under licence in Japan by Mitsubishi.

53 Westland Scout and Wasp

The helicopter 'twins' produced by Westland as the Scout and Wasp originated in November 1957 with a Saunders-Roe private venture design for a Skeeter development and replacement. Two prototypes of the aircraft, then known as the Saro P.531, were begun in early 1958, the first (G-APNU) flying on 20 July and the second (G-APNV) on 30 September 1958. Several Skeeter components were used in their construction, including the tailboom, short-legged tricycle undercarriage and rotor blades (the P.531 having a 4-blade assembly). Both prototypes were powered by Blackburn-built Turmo 603 turboshaft engines, derated to 325 shp.

Westland, after acquiring Saunders-Roe in 1959, took development an important stage further by completing two more prototypes with double the power and various other changes including a skid undercarriage. A Blackburn A129 (later known as the Nimbus) derated to 635 shp powered G-APVL, which flew on 9 August 1959, while G-APVM, flown on 3 May 1960, was given a Gnome H.1000 engine derated to 685 shp.

The first firm order for this general purpose helicopter came from the Army Air Corps, a pre-series batch of P.531-2 Mk 1's basically similar to G-APVL being ordered in 1959. The first of these was flown on 4 August 1960, and in the following month a substantial Army order was placed for the type as the Scout AH Mk 1. Delivered from spring 1963, these are 5-seaters with Nimbus 101 or 102 engines and skid landing gear. They replaced the Skeeter both in the UK and abroad and are employed for passenger or freight transport, liaison, search and rescue, and training. The Scout can also be used for casualty evacuation, carrying 2 stretchers inside the cabin and 2 more supported externally. Up to the spring of 1968 about one hundred and fifty Scouts were built, these including deliveries to the Royal Australian Navy (two for shipborne survey work), Royal Jordanian Air Force (three), and the police departments of Bahrain (two) and Uganda (two).

Parallel development of the Wasp anti-submarine version took somewhat longer, due to exhaustive naval trials carried out from November 1959 with a modified G-APNV and two specially-built P.531-0/N's, which also had Turmo engines but were fitted with a long-stroke quadricycle wheel undercarriage as well as landing skids. The Wasp is designed to operate from platforms on the rear decks of frigates, primarily as an extension of the ships' ability to attack submarines, but carrying no search gear. The first flight by a production Wasp was made on 28 October 1962. This version differs from the Scout in having a 710 shp (derated) Nimbus 103 or 104 engine, long-stroke, fully-castoring wheel undercarriage (but no skids) and a half-tailplane at the top of the tail rotor pylon on the starboard side. (The Scout has a full tailplane below the tailboom.) The Wasp's main rotor blades and its entire tail section can be folded for stowage on ship. A weapon load of some 540 lb (244 kg) can be attached to the underside between the undercarriage legs; this may comprise two Mk 44 homing torpedoes or an equivalent weight of depth charges or bombs. The Wasp HAS Mk 1 entered service in October 1963, and first production aircraft were allocated to No 829 Squadron and deployed singly aboard the Royal Navy's *Tribal* class and *Leander* class frigates. Other Wasps have been ordered by the navies of Brazil (three), the Netherlands (twelve), New Zealand (three) and South Africa (seventeen).

54 & 55 **Bell Model 47**
In one form or another the Bell 47 has been in continuous production

since late 1945, the total output by Bell and its foreign licensees having reached around five thousand of these remarkably long-lived aircraft by the end of 1967, to make the type the world's most widely-built helicopter by a comfortable margin. Production was still continuing in 1972.

The original Bell 47 was the production version of Bell's first helicopter, the experimental Model 30. The first of five Bell 30 prototypes, all with 165 hp Franklin engines, was flown in 1943, and the first of an initial ten Bell 47's, with a 178 hp Franklin, was flown on 8 December 1945. The CAA type approval cerficate granted to this aircraft on 8 March 1946 was the first ever awarded to a commercial helicopter anywhere in the world. Large-scale production, initiated in 1946, began with the military Bell 47A and civil 47B, both with 178 hp Franklins. Sixteen 47A's were completed for US Army evaluation, and two for the USAAF, with the designation YR-13; ten similar HTL-1's were tested by the US Navy. A car-type enclosed cabin seating two crew members side by side was standard on most early A and B models, but a utility/agricultural version, the 47B-3, had open crew positions. From this was developed the Bell 47D, first variant to introduce the 'goldfish bowl' moulded canopy, and this new model was certificated by the FAA on 25 February 1948. It also formed the subject of the first substantial military order, the US Army receiving sixty-five H-13B's, of which it had sixteen converted to

an ambulance version as the H-13C, and the US Navy ordering twelve HTL-2's. In 1949 the Bell 47D-1 appeared with an openwork tail-boom (as on the H-13C) and an underfin. Eighty-seven 2-seat H-13D's and four hundred and ninety 3-seat dual-control H-13E's to this configuration were supplied to the US Army, their US Navy counter-parts being the HTL-4 (forty-six) and HTL-5 (thirty-six). The Navy's HTL-3 (nine delivered) corresponded to the Model 47E, a 2-seater with a 200 hp Franklin 6V4-200-C32 engine; while the Army's XH-13F (Bell Model 201) was a solitary test-bed for a Continental T51 turbine engine.

It was the 200 hp Franklin engine, combined with the 3-seat capacity of the 47D-1, that gave rise to the Model 47G, which was granted an FAA type certificate in June 1953 and was still in production in its later forms in 1972. The US Army's H-13G (now OH-13G), two hundred and sixty-five of which were built, corresponds to this model, as does the Navy's HTL-6, of which forty-eight were built.

The first departure from the use of Franklins appeared in the 1955 Bell 47G-2, whose 200 hp Lycoming VO-435 enabled it to operate at higher weights without losing performance. The Bell 47G series are named Sioux by the US Army, which received more than four hundred and fifty of the G-2 model designated H-13H (now UH-13H). Two of these were later converted to G-3 standard as H-13K's. A more powerful VO-435 of 240 hp was installed in the G-2A, which was followed in 1963 by the similarly powered 47G-2A-1 having a wider cabin with separate seats, improved rotor blades and extra fuel tankage. Boosted variants included the G-3 (supercharged Franklin 6VS-335-A of 225 hp) and G-3B (turbo-supercharged Lycoming TVO-435 of 280 hp). More than three hundred OH-13S's and four hundred and fifteen dual-control TH-13T's for the US Army are generally equivalent to the G-3B. The 47G-4 and G-5 are 3-seat utility versions with non-supercharged engines, the former having a 280 hp Lycoming VO-540 and the latter a 265 hp VO-435. A 2-seat agricultural version of the 47G-5 is known as the Ag-5. Updated commercial versions still being produced by Bell in 1972 are the 47G-3B-2A (270 hp supercharged Lycoming) and 47G-5A (265 hp Lycoming).

Two parallel attempts were made in 1954 to produce a modernised version of the 47G. The first of these, the Bell 47H-1, met with limited success and comparatively few were built. The Bell 47J (originally known as the 47G-1) also had a fully enclosed fuselage, with a new car-type cabin, but the carrying capacity was increased to 4 persons plus baggage and the power-plant was the 220 hp version of the VO-435 engine. Known as the Bell Ranger, the 47J series was produced chiefly to meet civil orders, though small quantities have been supplied as UH-13J VIP transports for the US Air Force (two),

UH-13P's for general duties with the US Navy (twenty-eight), and HH-13Q rescue helicopters for the US Coast Guard (two). Two others, designated UH-13R, served as test-beds for Allison T63 turbine engines. Eighteen TH-13N (Bell 47K) trainers for the US Navy were 2-seaters with dual controls and IFR equipment, but were otherwise similar to the UH-13P. Civil models, from the 47J-2 of 1960, have had hydraulically powered controls and metal rotor blades as standard equipment. Production by Bell of the 47J series ended in 1966, but variants of the G and J series are still being built in Italy and Japan (see below).

In 1952 Agusta in Italy acquired a licence to manufacture the Bell 47 in Europe, its first example (a 47G) flying on 22 May 1954. Since then Agusta has produced over a thousand examples of G and J variants, including two 'Super Ranger' versions of its own. These are the 4/5-seat 47J-3 with a 270 hp (derated) VO-540 and the high altitude 47J-3B-1 with a 270 hp TVO-435. Agusta supplied fifty Model 47G-3B-1's to the British Army, and components for a further two hundred and fifty which were assembled by Westland as the Sioux AH Mk 1. A torpedo-armed anti-submarine version of the J-3 was evolved for evaluation by the Italian Navy. A 3-seat development of the 47G, designed by Agusta, was flown in May 1970 and is being developed and produced by Agusta's subsidiary, Elicotteri Meridionali, as the EMA 124. It is powered by a

250 hp (derated) Lycoming VO-540 engine.

Bell's other principal licensee is Kawasaki in Japan. Between 1953 and 1 January 1971 this company delivered eleven Model 47D's and two hundred and twenty-seven Model 47G's to customers in Brazil, Burma, Japan, Korea, the Philippines, Taiwan and Thailand. Kawasaki had also produced, by the same date, one hundred and eighty-four examples of the KH-4, its own development of the Bell 47G-3B with an enlarged 4-seat cabin and a derated TVO-435 engine giving 260 hp.

Specialised conversions of standard Bell 47's, of which small numbers have been produced, include the Carson Super C-4, based on the 47G or G-2 with a 240 hp Franklin 6VS-335-A giving boosted performance; and El Tomcat, a single-seat agricultural model converted by Continental Copters Inc, with spray bars, skid landing gear and a much-simplified cabin and tailboom structure.

56 Aérospatiale Alouette III

Basically, the Alouette III is an enlarged and more powerful development of the Alouette II, with a more powerful turboshaft engine and a strengthened transmission system. The cabin is enlarged to accommodate a pilot and 6 passengers, and the tailboom is an enclosed, semimonocoque structure. First flown on 28 February 1959, the SE 3160 Alouette III embodied several of the features seen during the preceding two years in earlier Sud-Est designs. First of these to fly, on 10 May 1957, was the SE 3131 Gouverneur (F-WIEA), which was basically an Alouette II with an Artouste engine, covered fuselage and executive cabin seating 5 occupants including the pilot. The SE 3140, flown on 16 May 1957, was fundamentally a Turmo-engined Alouette II and the SE 3150 an Artouste-powered development of it.

Series production of the Alouette III began in 1961, after two prototype and two pre-series machines had been built, and the aircraft received domestic type approval on 12 December 1961. By the beginning of 1972, one thousand and thirty-two Alouette III's had been ordered. The SA 316B, which superseded the SE 3160 at the start of 1970, has an 870 shp Artouste IIIB engine, derated to 550 shp. From the beginning of 1972 this was supplanted in production by the SA 316C, which has an Artouste IIID derated to 600 shp. The SA 319B, which appeared in 1967, differs principally from the SA 316C in having an Astazou XIV engine, derated from 870 shp to 600 shp.

Most Alouette III's are for military customers, including the armed forces of Abu Dhabi (five), Argentina (four), Austria (eleven), Bangla Desh (three), Burma (thirteen), Denmark (eight), Dominican Republic (one), Ecuador (six), Equatorial Guinea (two), Ethiopia (ten), Hong Kong (two), India (one hundred and twenty-two), Indonesia (ten or more), Iraq (twelve), Irish Republic (four), Israel (approx fifteen), Ivory Coast (three), Jordan (seven), Khmer (eight), Laos (four),

Lebanon (seven), Malagasy (two), Malaysia (twenty-nine), Mexico (ten), Morocco (seven), Nepal (one), the Netherlands (seventy-seven), Pakistan (sixteen), Peru (twelve), Portugal (one hundred and ten), Rhodesia (twelve), Saudi Arabia (six), Singapore (eight), South Africa (seventy), Switzerland (eighty-three), Tunisia (four), Venezuela (twenty), Yugoslavia (twenty) and Zaire (fifteen). In France, the ALAT is the prime user with eighty-four; the Armée de l'Air has eighty-two, the Aéronavale twenty-two. Manufacturing licences were held in 1972 by HAL in India (eighty), IRMA in Romania (fifty) and the Federal Aircraft Factory in Switzerland (sixty).

Duties of the Alouette III include those of tactical or assault transport, flying crane (with 750 kg = 1,653 lb external sling load) or casualty evacuation (with 2 passengers and 2 stretchers carried inside the cabin). Prototypes have also been flown of versions for armed close-support and anti-submarine duties.

57 Aérospatiale/Westland SA 341 Gazelle

The SA 341, whose SA 340 prototype F-WOFH flew for the first time on 7 April 1967, is a lightweight multi-purpose helicopter in the tradition of the ubiquitous Alouette. It is one of the types specified in the January 1967 Anglo-French helicopter agreement for large-scale production for the British and French armed forces. The first aircraft utilised the tail rotor and skid of the Alouette II and the engine

and transmission system of the Alouette II Astazou, but the second prototype (F-ZWRA, first flown on 17 April 1968) was more representative of production Gazelles in having an Astazou IIN2 and a 'solid' vertical fin within which rotates a 13-blade 'fenestron' or shrouded-fan tail rotor. The main rotor blades were developed in collaboration with Bölkow of Germany. The cabin will seat 5 occupants, including the pilot(s).

By late 1972 total orders for the Gazelle had reached two hundred and forty, and seven versions had been announced. These include the British Army AH Mk 1 (SA 341B), Royal Navy HT Mk 2 (SA 341C), and Royal Air Force HT Mk 3 and HCC Mk 4 (SA 341D and E); the SA 341F for the French Army; the civil SA 341G; and the SA 341H military export version. The first flight by a production Gazelle was made on 6 August 1971, and French certification was granted on 6 June 1972. The Gazelle is to be marketed in the USA by Vought Helicopters, which has ordered twenty SA 341G's, and licence manufacture is to be undertaken by Soko in Yugoslavia.

58 MBB BO 105

Design of the BO 105 lightweight general purpose helicopter was begun by Bölkow (now a constituent of Messerschmitt-Bölkow-Blohm) in July 1962, utilising basic experience gained by the company in the preceding few years in building the BO 102 and BO 103. The former was a non-flying, ultra-light helicopter trainer, and the BO 103, flown for the first time on 9 September 1961, was essentially the same aircraft minus its fixed base. An enlarged version of the BO 103 was proposed as the BO 104, but this project was supplanted by the more promising BO 105.

The first BO 105 prototype, powered by a pair of Allison 250-C18 turboshaft engines and using a conventional hinged-rotor installation, encountered ground resonance problems which eventually caused its destruction. The second prototype, which flew for the first time on 16 February 1967, was similarly powered but introduced the 4-blade rigid rotor which is standard on production aircraft. The third prototype (first flight 20 December 1967) was powered by two MAN-Turbo 6022 turboshafts. Two pre-production aircraft followed, one of which had 400 shp Allison 250-C20 engines, and a choice of the -C18 or -C20 is available to purchasers of production BO 105's. In addition to the pilot the BO 105 will accommodate 4 or 5 passengers with their baggage; orders for about sixty had been placed by early 1972, by which time about a dozen had been delivered. The BO 105 is certificated for operation in the United States, where Boeing holds a manufacturing and marketing licence. The non-articulated rotor, whose foldable blades are reinforced with glassfibre, was developed over several years by Bölkow in association with Sud-Aviation and was initially flight-tested on one of the latter company's Alouette II Astazou helicopters.

59 Fairchild Industries FH-1100

In May 1961 the Hiller Model 1100 was one of three designs selected by the US Army for prototype evaluation in its LOH (Light Observation Helicopter) competition announced two years previously. Five HO-5 prototypes (later redesignated OH-5A) were ordered, powered by 250 shp Allison T63-A-5 turboshafts engines, and the first of these (N81005) made its maiden flight on 21 January 1963. The OH-5A was designed as a 4-seater carrying a pilot and either 3 passengers or a 400 lb (181 kg) payload.

The LOH contract was eventually won by the Hughes OH-6A, but Hiller, which became a subsidiary of Fairchild Stratos in May 1964, decided in February 1965 to offer the helicopter in the civil market. Certification to FAA standard, required of all entrants in the LOH competition, was granted to the Model 1100 on 20 July 1964, and the FH-1100 represents a considerable advance over contemporary rivals in terms of speed, range and general performance.

Some of the Army prototypes were reworked as civil demonstrators, and production of an initial run of 250 machines was continuing in 1972. The first production FH-1100 was completed in June 1966, delivery beginning shortly afterwards. The largest civil operator is Okanagan of Canada, which has thirty. Sixteen were supplied to the Royal Thai Police Department, and military users include the Argentine Army (seven), Brazilian Navy (six), Chilean Army (two), and the air forces of Cyprus (one), Ecuador (one), Panama (three), the Philippines (eight) and Salvador (one).

The Model 1100 is offered as a utility 5-seater (including the pilot) for executive, business and general use. Powerplant is the Allison 250-C18, civil version of the T63 engine.

60 Kaman H-2 Seasprite

Winner of a 1956 US Navy competition for a fast, long range all-weather utility helicopter, the Kaman Model K-20 Seasprite entered production in 1961, initial models consisting of eighty-eight UH-2A's (originally HU2K-1) and one hundred and two UH-2B's. These were preceded by four prototypes, the first of which (147202) was flown for the first time on 2 July 1959, powered by a 1,025 shp T58-GE-6 turboshaft engine. Powerplant of the UH-2A and B is a single 1,250 shp T58-GE-8.

These Seasprites replaced earlier piston-engined helicopters for a range of duties that included reconnaissance, supply, carrier 'plane guard', communications, ship-to-shore transport and casualty evacuation, although the principal role was that of search and rescue. Flown by a crew of 2, the Seasprite can accommodate up to 11 passengers or 4 stretchers in the cabin, and has a watertight body for landings at sea. In flight, the wheeled undercarriage is fully retractable, emphasising the aircraft's unusually clean lines. The UH-2A had more comprehensive electronics and navigational equipment than the UH-2B and was able to operate in all weathers. First UH-2A deliveries were made to the US Navy's squadron HU-2 in December 1962, and the type first went to sea aboard USS *Independence* in June 1963. The UH-2B followed suit, with Detachment 46 of HU-4 in USS *Albany*, two months later, and both types have been employed extensively in the Pacific and Southeast Asia.

In March 1965 Kaman completed the first of two UH-2B conversions in which two T58-GE-8B's were installed, in pods on either side of the rotor pylon, to give the Seasprite a more sustained performance and twin-engined reliability. Starting in 1967, existing UH-2A's and -2B's were converted to similar configuration, with slightly more tail area and minor alterations to the cockpit and rotor pylon; they were then re-designated UH-2C. About sixty such conversions had been delivered by the end of 1970. The UH-2C and all subsequent models now have twin 1,350 shp T58-GE-8F engines.

A small batch of UH-2's was acquired by the US Army, which named the aircraft Tomahawk. One of these (14-9785), with a 1,500 shp T58-GE-10 engine, was evaluated in an armed ground support role, and another (14-7978) was evaluated in the mid-1960s as a high-speed compound helicopter, with a 2,500 lb (1,134 kg) st YJ85 turbojet pod on the starboard side of the cabin and later with small fixed wings to off-load the main rotor. This aircraft was flown at 216 mph (348 km/hr) before the stub wings were fitted. Neither of these achieved production status, but six examples were delivered to the US Navy, for operation in Southeast Asia, of an armed and armoured version known as the HH-2C. Operable at an overload take-off weight of 12,800 lb (5,806 kg), these have an improved main rotor assembly, a 4-blade tail rotor and twin-wheel main landing gear units. They are employed for search and rescue operations in combat areas and are armed with a chin-mounted Minigun turret and waist-mounted machine-guns. The HH-2D, of which fifty were delivered to the USN from February 1970, is a similar conversion from earlier single-engined models, having the structural improvements of the HH-2C but lacking the guns and armour protection.

One of the US Navy's most important priority programmes of recent years is that concerned with LAMPS (Light Airborne Multi-Purpose System) aircraft for anti-submarine warfare and anti-ship missile defence missions. As part of this programme Kaman had by mid-1972 modified twenty HH-2D Seasprites to LAMPS configuration under the new designation SH-2D, and conversion of a further twenty-five was to follow. The first SH-2D was flown on 16 March 1971; deliveries of the first twenty began in the following summer and were completed in March 1972. This version became operational with a detachment of Squadron HC-4 in November 1971, and by spring 1972 was operational with both the Atlantic and Pacific Fleets. The SH-2D has a powerful under-nose search radar and MAD gear, and carries ESM (electronic support measures), active and passive sonobuoys, smoke markers, flares and an MK-46 homing torpedo. The US Navy hopes eventually to convert its entire inventory of Seasprite helicopters for LAMPS missions, in addition to which it is expected to require additional helicopters as new warships are added to the fleet. In anticipation of the latter requirement two YSH-2E prototypes of an advanced LAMPS version were undergoing tests in 1972 (first flight 7 March), and as a follow-on type Kaman has evolved a design known as the Sealamp, with advanced search radar and other avionics, internally-stowed MAD gear and provision for externally-mounted weapons.

61 Aérospatiale/Westland SA 330 Puma

The first discussions which led to the evolution of the SA 330 took place in 1962, when France's Armée de Terre made known its requirements for a minimum-size tactical and logistics transport helicopter capable of all-weather operation. At about this time Sud-Aviation was completing two modified examples of the Sikorsky S-58 (which Sud had been building under licence), each of which was fitted with a 1,900 shp Turboméca Bi-Bastan turboshaft engine, and the first of these flew on 5 October 1962. The S-58 development was not pursued, but the SA 330 as first envisaged was to have been powered by two 1,300 shp Bastan VII's and able to transport 12 troops.

When development of the SA 330 and the production of seven test aircraft (two prototypes and five pre-series machines) was authorised by the STAé in June 1963, Turmo III free turbines of the same rating were selected in preference to the Bastan powerplant. The evaluation aircraft were allotted civil registrations F-ZWWN to 'WT, and the first of them made its maiden flight on 15 April 1965; all of these, plus a sixth pre-series aircraft, were flying by summer 1968, and the first production aircraft was flown in September 1968. By that time the Puma had become, with the SA 341 Gazelle and the Westland-designed W.G.13 Lynx, one of the three helicopters covered by an Anglo-French agreement signed in 1967, and had been selected as the RAF's tactical transport helicopter. Orders up to late 1972 included one hundred and thirty SA 330B's for the Aviation Légère de l'Armée de Terre, delivery of which began in spring 1969; and forty SA 330E's (Puma HC Mk 1) for the Royal Air Force, delivery of which began in autumn 1971. These are powered by 1,328 shp Turmo IIIC4 turboshaft engines. A military export version, designated SA 330C, has Turmo IVB engines, and has been ordered by Abu Dhabi (three), Ivory Coast (one), Mexico (three), Portugal (twelve), South Africa (twenty or more) and Zaire (thirty). The SA 330F is a civil passenger or cargo transport version, first flown on 26 September 1969 and powered by 1,290 shp Turmo IVA engines.

Although intended primarily as a combat support transport, the Puma may also be employed in the ambulance role, accommodating 6 stretchers and 4 sitting casualties; or as a flying crane, with a 2,500 kg (5,510 lb) external load. In the transport role it can carry up to 20 troops. Other applications include mountain rescue, with a hoist capable of lifting a 275 kg (606 lb) load, or executive transport with a 9/12-seat luxury cabin. It carries a crew of 2. The main rotor blades fold back to facilitate stowage, and all landing wheels retract, although they protrude slightly as a safeguard for emergency landings.

62 Agusta A 109 Hirundo (Swallow)

The Agusta designation A 109 was applied originally to a project announced in the mid-1960s for a 7/8-seat general-purpose helicopter, powered by a single turboshaft engine in the 700 shp range and having a tadpole-shaped fuselage with an under-fuselage vertical fin. This gave way in 1967 to the A 109C design, with modified fuselage contours and a powerplant of two Allison 250-series turbine engines. In its eventual form, as illustrated, it has undergone considerable further revision in outline, the designation has reverted to A 109, and the aircraft has been named Hirundo. The Hirundo is a private venture by Agusta, which initiated three flying prototypes and a static and fatigue test airframe. The first prototype

(NC7101) flew for the first time on 4 August 1971, but was severely damaged during later flight testing.

The general concept remains that of an 8-seat general-purpose helicopter, the main cabin accommodating up to 6 passengers, with seats for 1 or 2 persons on the flight deck. In passenger configuration, the enlarged rear fuselage provides a generous baggage compartment; alternatively, the Hirundo can be used as an ambulance (2 stretchers and 2 medical attendants), freighter (with internal load or with 2,205 lb = 1,000 kg capacity under-fuselage cargo sling), rescue aircraft (with 330 lb = 150 kg capacity rescue hoist on the port side), or in an armed role with four TOW missiles, fourteen 2·75 in rockets or two machine-gun pods mounted on external pylons.

63 Mil Mi-8 ('Hip')

The Mi-8 appeared in prototype form towards the end of 1961. In broad terms it bears the same relationship to the Mi-4 as the Mi-2 has to the Mi-1, and (initially at least) the rotor hub, rotor blades, rear fuselage boom and certain undercarriage components were similar to those employed in the Mi-4. The original prototype was powered by a single 2,700 shp Soloviev turboshaft mounted over the cabin roof, but in the second machine, which flew for the first time on 17 September 1962, this was replaced by two smaller Isotov engines of 1,500 shp each (later 1,700 shp). The latter became the

standard installation on production aircraft, the only other major design change being the substitution of a 5-blade rotor for the original 4-blade one in 1964.

The Mi-8 carries a 2- or 3-man crew and has seating accommodation for up to 28 passengers in its standard airline form. Alternative internal arrangements include a 9-passenger de luxe saloon cabin for executive travel (this version being known as the Mi-8 Salon) or a cargo layout for an internal payload of 4,000 kg (8,818 lb). Quick-change conversion of the cargo model to a passenger carrier can be carried out by installing 24 tip-up seats along the cabin sides. Clam-shell rear doors are provided for loading large items of cargo or, in the ambulance role, 12 stretchers which can be carried with an accompanying medical attendant. The Mi-8 can also be used as a rescue machine with a winch on the cabin side capable of lifting a 200 kg (440 lb) load, or with an under-fuselage hook for an external sling load of 3,000 kg (6,614 lb). It is known to have been in use with the Soviet Air Force since at least 1967, and also serves with the air forces of Czechoslovakia, Egypt, Ethiopia, East Germany, Hungary, India, Iraq, Pakistan, Peru, Poland, Sudan and Syria. The military versions have smaller, circular cabin windows and provision for carrying externally-mounted weapons. Aeroflot uses the civil versions for passenger transport, for transport and patrol/survey duties in the Antarctic, and for air ambulance duties.

64 Aérospatiale SA 321 Super Frelon

France's largest production helicopter originated with two prototypes of the SA 3200 Frelon (Hornet), the first of which was flown on 10 June 1959. Completed to a multi-service specification, the SA 3200 was powered by three 750/800 shp Turmo IIIB turboshaft engines and had a swing-tailed rear fuselage. Two large external tanks held the fuel, leaving the entire cabin free to accommodate up to 28 troops. Each engine supplied independent drive to the rotor head, thus ensuring twin-engined capability if one unit should fail. However, further development of the Frelon lapsed in favour of the SA 3210 (now SA 321) Super Frelon, a more advanced and more powerful version developed with assistance, especially with the rotor system, from Sikorsky.

Major differences revealed by the two Super Frelon prototypes included a watertight boat-type hull with a rear-loading ramp instead of the swing-tail, although the extreme rear of the tailboom and the 6-blade main rotor can be folded for stowage purposes. The SA 3210-01 (F-ZWWE), which first flew on 7 December 1962, was powered by three 1,320 shp Turmo IIIC2 engines, and in July 1963 set up several international records, including one for a speed in a straight line of 350·47 km/hr (217·77 mph) that remained unbeaten until 1970. The second prototype, fitted out to l'Aéronavale requirements, had stabilising floats incorporating search radar, dipping sonar and other anti-submarine equipment. Four pre-series Super Frelons were followed by the flight of the first production machine on 30 November 1965 and by the start of deliveries of twenty-four SA 321G's to l'Aéronavale in early 1966. These can carry four homing torpedoes or other anti-submarine stores, or gear for minesweeping, minelaying or ship towing; they are allocated to Flottille 32F, and duties include operations from the helicopter carrier *Jeanne d'Arc* and coastal patrol around the bases for France's *Redoutable* class nuclear submarines. Twelve SA 321K transports have been supplied to the Israel Defence Force, sixteen Super Frelons to the South African Air Force, sixteen to Iran and nine to Libya.

A commercial utility and transport version, the SA 321J, is in current production, having flown for the first time on 6 July 1967. Certificated on 20 October 1967, the SA 321J can be used as a 27-seat passenger transport, as a freighter with a 4,000 kg (8,818 lb) internal or 5,000 kg (11,023 lb) externally-slung payload, or for firefighting or other duties; at least one is acting as a supply transport to offshore oil drilling operations. The SA 321JA, certificated in December 1971, is generally similar but has a higher take-off weight. On 7 April 1967, the prototype SA 321F (F-WMHC) made its maiden flight. This is an enlarged-capacity passenger version with seating for up to 37 occupants and large sponson-type fairings amidships which act as baggage holds.

65 Sikorsky S-64 Skycrane/CH-54 Tarhe

Sikorsky's first crane helicopter, the S-60, was a research vehicle designed and built from funds shared between the US Navy and the parent company. Work on the design started in May 1958, the S-60 being given the powerplant, rotor and transmission systems of the S-56 helicopter. The 2,100 hp Pratt & Whitney R-2800 engines were mounted in outrigged pods into which the main undercarriage wheels could be partially retracted. The S-60, registered N807, first flew on 25 March 1959 and was demonstrated extensively until it was lost during a test flight in April 1961.

By this time, however, Sikorsky had already begun to build a prototype of the bigger S-64A, and this machine (N325Y) was flown on 9 May 1962. The S-64A retained the same basic rotor system as the S-60, though employing a 6-blade main rotor. It differed from the smaller machine in having a pair of 4,050 shp JFTD12A turboshafts mounted side-by-side on top of the fuselage boom, and had no fin area below the boom. Ground clearance beneath this boom is 9 ft 4 in (2·84 m) and the main wheel track is 19 ft 9 in (6·02 m), hence loads of considerable size can be fitted underneath the S-64A. The landing gear can be lengthened and shortened hydraulically, so that the helicopter can 'crouch' on to its load, raise it off the ground and then, if desired, taxi with it to a more suitable take-off point. Two additional prototypes, N305Y and N306Y, were completed for evaluation by the Federal German forces. Re-registered D-9510 and D-9511, they were operated under the aegis of the former Weser Flugzeugbau.

After evaluation of the original prototype at Fort Benning, Georgia, the US Army placed a pre-series order in June 1963 for six S-64A's with the military designation CH-54A (originally YCH-54A). Five of these were delivered in 1964–65 and operated with the 478th Aviation Company supporting the US Army's 1st Cavalry Division in Vietnam. Eighteen more CH-54A's (Army name Tarhe) were ordered in 1966, and total orders for this version stood at about eighty in mid-1972, later aircraft having uprated -4A engines of 4,620 shp each. Loads which can be lifted by the S-64A/CH-54A include trucks or palletised containers holding a field hospital unit, 48 casualty litters, 67 troops or 22,890 lb (10,382 kg) of cargo. One CH-54A in Vietnam has successfully lifted 87 troops, and of three international height records set by the CH-54A in 1965, two were still unbeaten in 1972.

Meanwhile the Sikorsky-owned S-64A and the sixth aircraft of the US Army's original order were used to further the acceptance of the type for the civil market, for such operations as ship-to-shore loading or unloading of cargo vessels or support of oil drilling operations. Two aircraft for the latter role, designated S-64E, were delivered in 1968 to the

Rowan Drilling Co of Texas. During 1967, N325Y carried out tests with the 23-seat Budd XB-1 Skylounge pod, designed to speed connection between the airports of Los Angeles and the city centre, and Sikorsky has developed the UMP (Universal Military Pod) for the US Army versions, capable of carrying personnel or of being used as a mobile field surgical unit or air ambulance. In 1969 the US Army took delivery of two examples of the CH-54B, this version having a payload capacity increased to 25,000 lb (11,340 kg), improved structure and transmission, and two 4,800 shp JFTD12-5A engines. The commercial equivalent of the CH-54B is designated S-64F.

66 Mil Mi-6 ('Hook')

For more than ten years the Mi-6 remained, dimensionally at least, the world's largest helicopter, and it was also the first turbine-powered helicopter to go into production in the Soviet Union. The first of five prototypes, flown by Rafail Kaprelian, made its maiden flight in autumn 1957, originally without the shoulder-mounted stub wings which are normally fitted to production Mi-6's except when used in flying crane or fire-fighting roles. Considering the size of the machine, the flight development period of the Mi-6 was relatively short, and production is believed to have started in early 1960. During flight trials the Mi-6 established a number of impressive load-to-altitude and speed-with-payload records in 1959, most of which it bettered three years later

when it set a total of eleven new FAI world records. In one of these it lifted a payload of 20,117 kg (44,350 lb) – greater than the entire weight of the biggest helicopter outside of the Soviet Union, the Sikorsky S-64A – and in another, still unbeaten by mid-1972, it lifted 10,000 kg (22,046 lb) to a height of 4,885 m (16,027 ft). An initial batch of thirty production Mi-6's was undertaken, and by mid-1972 at least five hundred more had been produced. These are in both military and civil service inside the USSR and have also been supplied to the air forces of Bulgaria, Indonesia, North Vietnam and Egypt. As a military transport the Mi-6 is capable of carrying up to 65 armed troops and has large rear clamshell loading doors for heavy loads such as army vehicles, artillery tactical missiles, or large palletised items of freight. The Mi-6's in service with Aeroflot are employed mainly as freighters, in which role they have an internal capacity for 12,000 kg (26,455 lb) of payload. The standard passenger version seats 65 people normally, although up to 120 persons can be accommodated in a high density seating arrangement. If used as an ambulance, the Mi-6 can carry 41 stretchers and 2 medical attendants.

Despite the existence of the later Mi-10, the Mi-6 is still utilised in the flying crane role, when the stub wings (which provide some 20 per cent of the total lift) are usually omitted. The Mi-6 has already demonstrated publicly its ability to airlift such large items as the Vostok space capsule and has since been used in large engineering projects, such as bridge-laying or the transport of oil drilling rigs, etc. The under-fuselage hook can support an externally slung load of 9,000 kg (19,842 lb). The fire-fighting version can deliver several tons of water over a forest fire area, either by spraying the fire or by delivering it as a water 'bomber' through a ventral hatch.

67 Mil Mi-10 and Mi-10K ('Harke')

First demonstrated publicly at Tushino in July 1961, the Mi-10 is a flying crane development of the Mi-6, with which it shares a common powerplant and rotor system. The stub wings are omitted, and the fuselage has been redesigned with a shallower cabin and a deeper tail-boom to give a level and flat under-surface against which its various loads can be hoisted. A tall, four-legged undercarriage is fitted. The aircraft is normally flown by a flight crew of 3 men, and in addition to slung loads can accommodate up to 28 passengers in the cabin boom. Special wheeled platforms have been designed on which the Mi-10's loads can be manoeuvred into position and on which they remain during the airborne journey. Alternatively, the aircraft can taxi into position over the load for its attachment. Landings with an attached load are aided by the use of a closed-circuit TV system. Typical loads may include a large passenger coach, a prefabricated building or a large freight pallet. Believed to have

flown for the first time in 1960, the Mi-10 is thought to be in service both with the Soviet armed forces and with Aeroflot. One is operated in the USA by Petroleum Helicopters Inc.

Details were released in March 1966 of the Mi-10K, a modified version with a much shorter undercarriage and presumably developed to carry sling loads which are unsuitable for fitting under the belly of the Mi-10. This version is manned by only 2 crew members, one of whom occupies a rearward-facing gondola underneath the nose from which he can supervise the cargo during loading and in flight. The Mi-10 and Mi-10K are not thought to have been produced in very large numbers. At least one Mi-10K was fitted with a conventional tricycle undercarriage; this may have been the machine which in May 1965 established a load-to-altitude record by lifting a weight of 25,105 kg (55,347 lb) to a height of 2,840 m (9,318 ft). The Soloviev engines which power the Mi-10K are scheduled to reach an output of 6,500 shp each, which would enable the helicopter to lift a slung load of 14,000 kg (30,865 lb).

69 Sikorsky S-65A/H-53/Sea Stallion

Currently the largest and heaviest helicopter in the western world, the S-65A is something of a hybrid, its fuselage being, in essence, a scaled-up version of that used on the S-61R, while its rotor and transmission system and certain other dynamic components are inherited from the S-64 Skycrane. The flat-bottomed body is watertight, and has sponsons amidships in which are housed fuel tanks and the main undercarriage members when retracted. The nosewheel is also fully retractable. The S-65A carries a crew of 3 and can airlift 38 troops and their equipment, 24 casualty litters and 4 medical attendants, or some 8,000 lb (3,629 kg) of cargo within the fuselage. A let-down rear ramp provides access for such military loads as 2 jeeps, 2 Hawk missiles, or a 105 mm howitzer and its carriage. A slung load of some 13,000 lb (5,897 kg) can be lifted on an under-fuselage hook.

In August 1962 it was announced that the S-65A had been selected as a new ship-borne heavy assault transport for the US Marine Corps, with the military title CH-53A Sea Stallion. A prototype flew on 14 October 1964, and delivery of the first one hundred and six production CH-53A's began in September 1966. Since January 1967 the Sea Stallion has been serving in Vietnam. Standard powerplant is two T64-GE-6 turboshaft engines, though the 3,080 shp T64-GE-1 or 3,435 shp T64-GE-16 may be fitted. One CH-53A with T64-GE-16 engines has been flown at a gross weight of 51,900 lb (23,541 kg), of which 28,500 lb (12,927 kg) was payload and fuel.

The HH-53B, flown for the first time on 15 March 1967, has 3,080 shp T64-GE-3 engines, a rescue hoist, jettisonable auxiliary fuel tanks and a telescopic in-flight refuelling probe. It also has machine gun positions fore and aft. The HH-53B is employed by the Aerospace Rescue and Recovery Service of the US Air Force, and delivery of eight, ordered in September 1966, began in June 1967. It was followed by the improved HH-53C (fifty-eight built), powered by 3,435 shp T64-GE-7 engines and equipped for the recovery of Apollo spacecraft. An improved model for the US Marine Corps, designated CH-53D, has 3,695 shp T64-GE-412 or 3,925 shp T64-GE-413 engines and can carry up to 64 troops. For the US Navy, Sikorsky is producing the RH-53D for mine countermeasures duties, and was due to begin delivery of thirty in late 1972. Under development for the USN is the CH-53E, to be powered by three 4,390 shp T64-GE-415 turboshafts. Military S-65's have been exported to Austria (two) and Israel (ten), and one hundred and fifty-three are being licence-built for the Federal German armed forces as the CH-53G, under a programme managed by VFW-Fokker.

70 **Bensen rotorcraft**
Russian-born Igor Bensen is probably the world's leading exponent of lightweight, home-built rotorcraft. After many years in rotorcraft research with General Electric and Kaman, he formed the Bensen Aircraft Corporation in 1953. Its first product was the single-seat, ramjet-powered Mid-jet, tested in 1954, followed in 1955 by the B-4 Sky-Scooter which was powered by a 40 hp Nelson engine and could

carry a pilot and one passenger. Bensen's current range of do-it-yourself rotorcraft stem from the B-5 Gyro-Glider of 1954, which was a single-seat rotor-kite towed into the air at around 20 mph (30 km/hr) and obtained its lift by the flow of air over its autorotating rotor. From this factory-built prototype, Bensen evolved the B-6 and B-7, and from these evolved the standard production model, the B-8. This has a somewhat more sturdy construction and is available in single-seat or 2-seat form, either as a factory-built machine or in kit form for amateur construction. Two examples, designated X-25, have been supplied to the USAF for evaluation. The B-8W Hydro-Glider is a waterborne version mounted on twin floats.

Powered autogyro versions of the auto-kites were developed simultaneously, the first being the B-7M which first flew on 6 December 1955. This was followed on 8 July 1957 by the first B-8M (M = motorised) and by the first production B-8M on 9 October 1957. The B-8M is normally powered by a 72 hp McCulloch piston engine. Optional features include a 90 hp McCulloch or 64 hp Volkswagen engine, and a mechanical rotor drive enabling the autogyro to make jump starts. With the VW engine (first flight autumn 1967), the aircraft is known as the B-8V. An advanced B-8M, known as the Super Bug, has a more powerful rotor spin-up system, higher gross weight and other refinements. An agricultural version of the B-8M is known as the

B-8MA Agricopter, and flew for the first time in September 1969. Float versions of these aircraft are known as Hydro-Copters. In the mid-1960s Bensen developed a multi-engined version of the B-8M known as the B-11M Kopter-Kart. This was powered by six 10 hp McCulloch MC75 go-kart engines mounted in two rows of three behind the pilot's seat and driving vertical propellers in addition to the 2-blade rotor.

Bensen also produced two helicopter designs, the first being the B-9 Little Zipster, a lightweight single-seater with a 60 or 70 hp Mercury engine and twin 2-blade co-axial rotors. The B-9 was superseded by the B-13, flown for the first time (N4625S) on 4 March 1963. This had a single 2-blade main rotor, driven by a 70 hp Mercury engine, and an anti-torque tail rotor driven by two 10 hp West Bend piston engines. VTOL lifting platform designs have included the B-10 Prop-Copter, flown in prototype form (N56U) on 6 August 1958 and powered by two 72 hp McCullochs, each driving a horizontal propeller; and the B-12 Sky-Mat, which flew for the first time on 2 November 1961 and consisted of a trellis-like open metal framework with ten small 2-blade rotors, each driven by a 10 hp West Bend engine, and a pilot's position in the centre.

Output of the Bensen Aircraft Corporation continues, however, to concentrate upon the powered and unpowered versions of the B-8, many thousands of which have been sold in factory-built or kit form in the United States and other parts of the world.

71 Wallis autogyros

Believing that the small autogyro was potentially one of the best small, practical 'personal' aircraft that could be built, Wing Commander K. H. Wallis began exploratory work in the late 1950s to determine ways in which the safety and performance of such aircraft could be improved. He followed an entirely new design approach to the mechanical aspects of autogyro design, and arising out of his early research patented a number of novel features. These included an offset gimbal system for the rotor head, to provide 'hands and feet off' stability and to eliminate undesirable control effects; a high-speed flexible rotor spin-up shaft, with positive disengagement during flight; an automatic system of controlling the rotor drive on take-off, allowing power to be applied until the last moment; centrifugal teeter stops to control 'teetering' of the rotor blades; and a safe starting system for one-man operation. The first aircraft to embody these features was the prototype WA-116 Agile (G-ARRT), flown for the first time on 2 August 1961 and powered by a modified Mc-Culloch 4318, a piston engine intended originally for target drone applications. Because of military interest in such an aircraft, Wg Cdr Wallis had formed an association with Beagle Aircraft Ltd, which built four WA-116's (G-ARZA/B/C and 'ASDY), the first of which flew on 10 May 1962. After obtaining a Special Category C of A the first three of these aircraft, serialled XR942-944, underwent trials by the British Army as potential light liaison, 'flying dispatch rider' and observation aircraft. No military orders were received, however, and the aircraft were later sold to Wallis Autogyros Ltd, a company formed by Wg Cdr Wallis when he retired from the RAF in 1964 to devote all of his time to autogyros. A further six WA-116's have been built, one of which (G-AXAS, first flight 3 April 1969) was completed as the WA-116-T, a 2-seat trainer version with somewhat close tandem seating for pilot and pupil. An enclosed nacelle was added to G-ARRT in 1962, and is now standard on the WA-116.

Despite several later designs, described below, the WA-116 has remained potentially one of the most promising of the Wallis autogyros built up to 1972, and has done much useful work. On 11 May 1968, G-ARRT was flown to a new world altitude record for autogyros of 15,220 ft (4,639 m). This, on the power of the 72 hp McCulloch, more than doubled the previous record, and Wg Cdr Wallis is emphatic that the limit then reached was his own, due to the extreme cold and the lack of any extra oxygen, and not that of the aircraft. On 12 May 1969, in spite of a strong cross-wind, G-ARRT set up a new world speed record for autogyros of 111 mph (179 km/hr). This aircraft has since been fitted with a Wallis-McCulloch engine developing about

100 hp. Another significant achievement was that of the WA-116-T, which on 30 June 1971 flew at an all-up to empty weight ratio of 3·14 : 1, believed to be a record for any class of aeroplane. On a rather different plane, two WA-116's have become film stars, notably G-ARZB, which figured in the James Bond film *You Only Live Twice*. For its role in the film it was flown with an 'armament' which included two jettisonable 'flame-throwers' on each side of the tail, fourteen 1·75 in rockets in two packs on the fuselage sides, two air-to-air 'guided missiles' under the fuselage, two dummy 0·30 in machine-guns in the nose, firing blanks, and 50 parachute 'grenades'. The rockets, missiles and parachute grenades were actually fired or launched from the aircraft during filming.

To combine the Wallis design with a fully-certificated engine the WA-117, powered by a 100 hp Rolls-Royce Continental O-200-B engine, was started in 1964. A preliminary test vehicle (G-ATCV) flew on 24 March 1965, followed by the true WA-117 prototype (G-AVJV) on 28 May 1967. The latter quickly became a 'working' aircraft: with an all-up weight of some 700 lb (317·5 kg), and a current (1972) test-purposes never-exceed speed of 130 mph (209 km/hr), it has been used for many special photographic and reconnaissance roles. Operating by day and night, it has been used equipped with Hawker Siddeley Dynamics infra-red linescan. When fitted with special silencers the WA-117 is one of the most silent

aircraft, and took part in the 1970 Loch Ness investigation. In 1972, carrying four aerial cameras, it carried out 'false colour' photography for a coastal ecology study. One other WA-117 (G-AXAR), with a larger cockpit, has also been built. A version with a 130 hp Rolls-Royce Continental O-240 engine (G-AYVO), begun as the WA-117-S, was later redesignated WA-120 and made its first flight on 13 June 1971. It is intended as a long-range aircraft of good climb and cruise performance, and has a fully-enclosed cockpit.

Wallis experimental autogyros include the WA-118 Meteorite, a high-speed, high-altitude research project which first flew (G-ATPW) on 6 May 1966 with a 120 hp supercharged Meteor Alfa 1 engine. Intended for speeds of up to 200 mph (322 km/hr), it was later fitted with a modified engine, bubble canopy and other modifications and was rebuilt as G-AVJW, making a new 'first' flight on 9 August 1969. The designation WA-119 was allotted to an 'economy' version of the WA-116, intended to be powered by a modified Rootes (Hillman) Imp motor car engine of 40 hp. Work on this project began in 1966, and was brought to a satisfactory flight performance standard using the WA-116 airframe G-ASDY. However, the project was subsequently abandoned due to high noise level from the ungeared propeller, and in September 1971 G-ASDY's experimental Imp engine was replaced by a 60 hp Franklin 2A-120-A, the first fully-certificated aero-engine to be fitted to a WA-116. Other WA-116's are being fitted with this engine, with encouraging results. The latest project in 1972 was the WA-121, the smallest and most streamlined Wallis design to date. It is projected in three basic forms: as a racer (100 hp Wallis-McCulloch); for cross-country flying (60 hp Franklin); and for very high altitude flying (120 hp Meteor). Wallis autogyros are currently built only for special purposes and are not on public sale.

72 NHI H-3 Kolibrie (Humming-Bird)

The H-3 Kolibrie was an all-Dutch venture, the joint handiwork of Jan Meijer Drees and Gerard Verhage at the SOBEH (Foundation for the Development and Construction of an Experimental Helicopter) early in 1952. Their objective was to keep the design as simple as possible, and to this end they decided to use ram-jets for power, eliminating the need for a gearbox or rotor drive shaft. The main drawback to this system was the ramjet's rather high fuel consumption, although operating costs were kept to a minimum by using domestic paraffin as the basic fuel. Once the ramjets were ignited this could be fed from any of the four 100 litre (22 Imp gal) under-fuselage tanks by centrifugal force.

In May 1955 a prototype of the SOBEH design, the 2-seat H-2 (registration PH-NFI), was flown for the first time. In October 1955 the Nederlandse Helicopter Industrie was formed by Aviolanda and Kromhout to build and market the production form of this helicopter, as the H-3 Kolibrie. An H-3 proto-type was flown in May 1956, and in 1957 an initial batch of ten production aircraft was laid down, the first three of which were used for certification tests. These were powered by two 44 lb (20 kg) st TJ-5 ramjets, with a small 2 hp APU to spin the rotors up to 70 rpm for ignition. A second batch of ten was begun, these having 51 lb (23 kg) st TJ-5A ramjets, but it is not certain whether all were completed. Domestic certification was granted in March 1958, delivery taking place to the first two Dutch customers immediately afterwards. Other Kolibries were sold in Germany, Israel and the United Kingdom. One aircraft was used for survey and exploration work in New Guinea. The Kolibrie was particularly suitable for agricultural duties, for which it could be fitted with 15·00 m (49 ft 2½ in) spray booms, or for helicopter pilot training. Up to three of the ventral fuel tanks could be replaced by tanks holding chemicals for crop spraying purposes. The H-3 could carry a passenger beside the pilot, or alternatively two stretchers, or a 375 kg (827 lb) cargo load slung on an under-fuselage hook. Because of its high fuel consumption the Kolibrie was uneconomical to fly on non-productive flights, and a special 'helicar' was developed to transport it on such journeys; this vehicle could also be used as a mobile take-off and landing platform.

73 Helicopter Technik Sky-Trac

The first five designs evolved by Alfred Vogt of the Helicopter Technik Wagner since the company's formation in 1960 included two experimental helicopters, each powered by a 95 hp rotating-piston engine. One was a simple 2-seater with a skid undercarriage and pod-shaped body; the other was the Rotorcar III 'roadable' helicopter.

The latter was developed into the Aerocar, whose prototype also flew in 1965. This had a 4-seat cabin, a twin tail assembly, and four road wheels hydraulically driven from the Oredon IV engine mounted behind the rotor pylon; but this project now appears to have been discarded.

From the former design Wagner produced the Sky-Trac torqueless helicopter, which is basically a chassis frame carrying the engine and rotor system, to which a variety of cabins or equipment can be fitted to fulfil different roles. Prototypes of the Sky-Trac 1 (D-HAJE) and Sky-Trac 3 (D-HAJI) were exhibited publicly at the Hanover Air Show in May 1966, the former having flown for the first time in July 1965; it received German certification in 1969. Both are powered by similar Franklin piston-engines, the Sky-Trac 1 being a single-seater with a 'goldfish bowl' moulded canopy, open at the rear, and the Sky-Trac 3 a 3-seater with a larger cabin faired-in at the back and underneath. Both aircraft were originally without a tail structure of any kind, but were each later fitted with an openwork tailboom supporting Vee tail surfaces. In 1972 a new company, Helicopter Technik München, was formed to produce the Sky-Trac 1 and to market it with a variety of 'mission kits' for agricultural or ambulance use, cargo transport and other duties. One such kit will permit conversion to seat a pilot and 2 passengers. A further development, known as the Sky-Rider, has also been announced: this is to be a 3/4-seat helicopter with a fully-enclosed fuselage and tailboom, and was displayed in mock-up form at the 1972 Hanover Air Show.

74 & 75 Kamov Ka-15 ('Hen') and Ka-18 ('Hog')

Nikolai Kamov's connection with rotorcraft development goes back to 1929, when he played a part in the design of the first successful Soviet Autogiro, the KaSkr-I. His partner in evolving this aircraft was N. K. Skrzhinskii, one of Russia's pioneer rotorcraft designers and chief aide to Aleksandir Yakovlev in the design of the tandem-rotor Yak-24. In the years following World War 2 Kamov, by then heading his own bureau, first occupied himself with small, ultra-light 'vozdushnye motorsikl' (airborne motor-cycle) designs having twin co-axial rotor systems. The first of these, the Ka-8, was flown in late 1947, but with only a 27 hp M-76 engine this aircraft was under-powered and only three prototypes were completed. An enlarged development, the Ka-10, flew in September 1949, with a 55 hp

Ivchenko AI-4V engine, driving two 3-blade co-axial rotors. The Ka-10 (later given the NATO code name 'Hat') was a single-seat aircraft with twin-pontoon landing gear and a single trapezoidal fin. Four Ka-10 prototypes were followed by eight Ka-10M's with longer pontoons and elliptical twin fins, and these were evaluated by the Soviet Navy for the ship-spotting role.

No production of the Ka-10M ensued, but a basically similar rotor system was utilised in Kamov's next design, the Ka-15, which made its first flight in 1952. This was a much larger helicopter, having an enclosed cabin seating 2 occupants side by side and being powered by a 255 hp Ivchenko AI-14V radial. The Ka-15 became known outside the USSR in 1955, at about the time that it began to enter Soviet service. The basic Ka-15 was built in some numbers for the Soviet forces, the major user being the Soviet Navy, which operated it from deck platforms. Other duties probably included communications, liaison and helicopter pilot training. The civil version, known as the Ka-15M, was also employed widely and was supplied to about a dozen countries outside the Soviet Union. Under the aegis of Aeroflot, the Ka-15M was employed within the USSR on work that included forestry and fishery patrol, agricultural, postal and taxi services; it could also be employed as an ambulance, with 2 stretchers mounted externally. From about 1960–61 the performance and payload capability of the Ka-15M was

improved by the installation of the 275 hp AI-14VF engine.

In the Ka-18, which first appeared publicly in the summer of 1957, the basic concept of the Ka-15 was taken a logical step further. The forward part of the fuselage, including the cabin, was redesigned and enlarged to accommodate up to 4 occupants including the pilot, and the tail assembly, generally similar to that of the Ka-15, was mounted at the rear of an elongated tail boom. The Ka-15 rotor system was retained, driven in the early Ka-18 production series by the same 255 hp Ivchenko AI-14V engine that powered the earlier design. Later Ka-18's were fitted with the AI-14VF version of this engine, offering an increased output of 275 hp and permitting an increase in gross weight to 1,500 kg (3,307 lb). Features of the Ka-18 included de-icing equipment and a full blind-flying panel, and American pilots who flew the helicopter described it as 'roomy and versatile'. A loading door in the nose allows a stretcher to be stowed in the cabin when aero-medical duties are carried out, while in an agricultural role the Ka-18 can be flown with external hoppers or spray booms for dry or liquid chemicals. Other specialised tasks have included aerial survey and ice, fishery or forestry patrol. A maximum freight load of 300 kg (661 lb) can be carried, with which the Ka-18's range is about 300 km (186 miles): with part of the payload replaced by 136 litre (30 Imp gal) auxiliary fuel tanks the range is increased to 750 km (466 miles).

Production of the Ka-18 was primarily on behalf of Aeroflot and Soviet civil authorities.

76 & 77 Kamov Ka-25 and Ka-25K ('Hormone')

Although it is clearly descended from the Ka-15/Ka-18 series of co-axial helicopters produced by the Kamov design bureau, the Ka-20 is a much larger machine and has a turbine powerplant. It was first seen by western observers at the Moscow Aviation Day display in July 1961, when a prototype version, the Ka-20 ('Harp'), took part in the fly-past. Early in 1960 the Soviet Union released a photograph showing a model of the projected atomic-powered ice-breaker *Lenin*, on whose after-deck was a helicopter of similar general appearance to the Ka-20. The example exhibited at Moscow in 1961 had a large search radar fairing beneath the front fuselage and a smaller fairing, possibly housing a navigational aid, under the tailboom. Pylons on the sides of the main cabin each carried a dummy missile some $7\frac{1}{2}$ ft ($2\frac{1}{4}$ m) in length. The Ka-25 production version does not appear to carry weapons externally, but has an internal bay large enough to carry conventional ASW weapons, including homing torpedoes. The four-wheel landing gear is fitted with a pontoon and a ring of small inflation bottles around each wheel, for emergency deployment in the event of a water landing. The primary role of the Ka-25 is that of anti-submarine helicopter, and the Soviet Navy's helicopter carrier/cruisers *Leningrad* and *Moskva*

each carry about twenty of these aircraft. The Ka-25 may also be employed for other duties such as transport or search and rescue, the cabin being large enough to accommodate about 12 passengers.

At Le Bourget in 1967 the Soviet authorities exhibited, for the first time outside the USSR, a civil derivative known as the Ka-25K. This is a flying crane helicopter, with a small gondola under the front fuselage in which a second crew member sits facing to the rear to supervise control of the externally-slung load during take-off, flight and landing. Maximum slung load of the Ka-25K is 2,000 kg (4,409 lb) over short distances. A passenger version can accommodate up to 12 people in tip-up seats arranged round the walls of the main cabin, and has a maximum range of 650 km (405 miles).

78 Kaman H-43 Huskie

As the Kaman Model 600, the Huskie won a US Navy design competition in 1950 and a contract was placed for it 'off the drawing board'. The K-600 was basically an enlarged development of Kaman's earlier HTK-1 and employed a similar system of contra-rotating, intermeshing rotors. The new type was required initially for liaison and general duties with the Marine Corps, by whom it was designated HOK-1. The first of two XHOK-1 prototypes flew on 27 September 1956, and delivery of eighty-one HOK-1's to the USMC began in April 1958. Twenty-four examples of the HUK-1, a utility model, were built for the US Navy itself, and eighteen H-43A's (first flight 19 September 1958) were completed for the US Air Force.

Accommodation in the original HOK-1 provided for a 2-man crew plus 5 passengers or 2 stretchers and 2 medical attendants, while the H-43A's, acquired for local crash and rescue duties at USAF airfields, could carry 2 fire-fighters and their equipment or 4 stretchers and a medical attendant. The H-43A, HUK-1 and HOK-1, redesignated HH-43A, UH-43C and OH-43D in 1962, were all powered by variants of the 600 hp R-1340 piston engine. The UH-43C and OH-43D were withdrawn from US Navy service in 1965. Following the employment of one HOK-1 as a testbed for the Lycoming XT53 turboshaft engine, two turbine-powered versions of the Huskie were selected for production.

The first of these was the H-43B (later HH-43B) rescue version, first flown on 13 December 1958. Powered by an 825 shp Lycoming T53-L-1B engine, and having an enlarged cabin seating up to 8 passengers, the HH-43B became the major production version of the Huskie, one hundred and ninety-three being built to meet USAF and MAP orders. Foreign air forces which received HH-43B's included those of Burma (twelve), Colombia (six), Morocco (four), Pakistan (six) and Thailand (three). In August 1964 the first flight took place of the HH-43F, an outwardly similar version which has a 1,150 shp T53-L-11A turboshaft derated to

825 shp, giving the Huskie an improved and sustained performance in 'hot and high' localities. Accommodation is rearranged to allow up to 11 passengers to be carried in addition to the pilot, and range is increased to 504 miles (810 km). Forty HH-43F's, including fourteen for the Imperial Iranian forces, were completed before Huskie production came to an end in 1965.

In August 1962 Kaman flew the prototype (N10029) of the twin-turbine K-1125 Huskie III, but development of this type was subsequently suspended.

79 **Kamov Ka-26 ('Hoodlum')**
The first indication that his bureau was working on the design of this twin-engined general-purpose utility helicopter was given by Nikolai Kamov himself in January 1964. The prototype of this aircraft, the Ka-26, was flown for the first time in 1965, followed by a small pre-series batch and the first production Ka-26's during 1966. In its general appearance the Ka-26 shows a marked similarity to the Kaman H-43 Huskie, except that it retains the typical Kamov-type 3-blade co-axial rotor arrangement, whereas the American machine has separate rotor heads and inter-meshing blades. The rotor blades and parts of the fuselage of the Soviet aircraft are of plastics and glassfibre construction.

The basic Ka-26 airframe comprises the 2-man crew cabin, rotor head and stub wings, with the engine pods at their extremities and twin tailbooms to the rear supporting the tail assembly. The tail unit is akin to that of a fixed-wing aeroplane, consisting of a tailplane and elevators, and fins and rudders with a pronounced toe-in angle. The piston-engined Ka-26 has three times the load-carrying ability of the earlier Ka-15, and considerable versatility of role is made possible by the use of interchangeable kits or units in the space behind the crew cabin and beneath the rotor head. These may take the form of a freight platform for a 900 kg (1,984 lb) load; a rescue winch, capacity 150 kg (330 lb); dust hoppers or liquid chemical tanks, also of 900 kg capacity, for agricultural dusting or spraying; a 'people pod' with a bench seat for 3 passengers along each side; or a similar cabin pod to accommodate 2 stretchers, 2 sitting patients and a medical attendant. The geological survey version shown in the illustration is characterised by a large electro-magnetic hoop aerial, and carries an externally-mounted magnetometer 'bird' which is towed by cable during operations. Other applications include Arctic search and rescue, aerial survey and mapping, and ice, fishery or forestry patrols, either from land bases or ships' platforms. The Ka-26 is normally equipped for single-pilot operation, but dual controls can be fitted if desired. The Ka-26 has been in widespread use in the Soviet Union since 1970, particularly as an agricultural aircraft employed over orchards and vineyards. By 1972 it was also in service, in various roles, in Bulgaria, Federal Germany, Hungary, Romania and Sweden.

80 Cierva CR.LTH-1 Grasshopper

The Cierva name, as recorded elsewhere in this volume, is an honoured one in the history of rotorcraft development. The original British-based Cierva Autogiro Co Ltd was formed in 1926, and prior to World War 2 built several successful types of Autogiro. After the war, in conjunction with G. and J. Weir Ltd, it was responsible for developing a number of early British helicopters, including the W.9 and the triple-rotor W.10 Air Horse. The company adopted its present title of Cierva Rotorcraft in 1965, after acquiring the company which was backing the Servotec Grasshopper helicopter designed by Dipl Ing J. S. Shapiro. This helicopter has since been radically modified and developed, via the Cierva Rotorcraft Mk III Grasshopper, into the current CR.LTH-1 prototype (G-AWRP) shown in the illustration.

This was the first CR.LTH-1 to fly, and was used for preliminary hovering trials during the first half of 1969. A second prototype (G-AXFM) flew for the first time on 18 August 1969, and both of these aircraft were powered by twin 145 hp Rolls-Royce Continental O-300-C piston engines. Construction began in the late summer of 1971 of a pre-production aircraft, initially to be fitted with 210 hp Continental IO-360-D engines, and two series production versions have been announced. These differ primarily in powerplant, and are known as the Twin 420 (two 210 hp Rolls-Royce Continental TSIO-

360-A) and the Twin 640 (two 320 hp Continental Tiara T6-320). The CR.LTH-1 has two co-axial contra-rotating 2-blade rotors, of semi-rigid 'teetering' type, whose unusually close separation is a major factor in the demonstrably low noise level of this helicopter. The aircraft is classed as a light utility helicopter, and is potentially suited to a variety of operational roles. The cabin shell and several other exterior panels are made of glass-fibre material, and the aircraft seats up to 5 people including the pilot. The rear bench seat (for 3 persons) can be removed if the aircraft is required for use as a cargo transport.

81 Piasecki HRP-1 Rescuer

Although it was built only in modest numbers and had an unspectacular (though useful) service career, the Piasecki HRP-1 has its place in the history of rotorcraft by virtue of being the world's first practical tandem-rotor helicopter and, at the time of its appearance, the world's largest helicopter of any kind. Frank N. Piasecki, holder of the first helicopter pilot's licence to be issued in the United States, became interested in rotorcraft development before America's entry into World War 2, and in 1943 he formed a company known as the P.V. Engineering Forum whose first design, the PV-2, was a single-seat, single main rotor helicopter with a 90 hp Franklin engine. This machine, which flew for the first time on 11 April 1943, was Piasecki's first and only single-rotor helicopter, for on 1 February 1944 he received a contract to develop a tandem-rotor utility transport and rescue aircraft for the US Navy.

Given the factory designation PV-3, this machine, powered by a Wright R-975 piston engine, made a successful first flight at Morton, Pennsylvania, in March 1945 and was followed by two XHRP-1 prototypes, one for US Navy flight trials and the other for static and dynamic tests. The test programme was completed in the spring of 1947, by which time the company title had changed to Piasecki Helicopter Corporation, and work had already begun on an initial batch of ten HRP-1 Rescuers ordered by the US Navy in June 1946. The first of these flew on 15 August 1947, and a second batch of ten was built later; they served with US Navy Squadrons HMX-1 and VX-3, the final machine being delivered in 1949. These were powered by 600 hp Pratt & Whitney R-1340-AN-1 engines. Twelve of the HRP-1's were eventually assigned to the US Marine Corps for assault training, while three others, as HRP-1G's, were used as rescue craft by the US Coast Guard. After withdrawal of the Rescuer from military service in the early 1950s, about six appeared on the US civil register.

The tandem-rotor layout offered a wider choice of c.g. positions, together with a small frontal area and a large lifting area; thus the HRP-1 was able to register a significant step forward, from craft whose main purpose had been to prove the flight principles of the helicopter, to a vehicle capable of doing a real job of work. Nicknamed – for obvious reasons – the 'flying banana', the HRP-1 carried a crew of 2 sitting in tandem, and its 400 cu ft (11·33 cu m) cabin could accommodate 8 passengers, 2,000 lb (907 kg) of cargo or 6 stretchers. The single engine was mounted in the rear part of the fuselage, with a clutch and gearbox amidships from which drive shafts ran to reduction gearboxes below each of the rotor hubs.

In June 1948 the US Navy ordered five examples of the much-developed PV-17 with the designation HRP-2. This had a considerably longer, redesigned fuselage with an all-metal skin (the HRP-1's front half was fabric-covered), a more roomy crew cabin with side-by-side seats, and modified rotor heads. This version formed the basis of the later PD-22 model which became the highly successful military Vertol H-21 series described separately.

82 **Bell Model 61 (HSL-1)**

The Bell HSL-1, although not a notably successful aeroplane, was the first helicopter designed from the outset for the submarine hunter/killer role. As the Bell Model 61, it was announced the winner of a US Navy design competition in June 1950, and an evaluation batch of three XHSL-1's (129133 to '35) was ordered shortly afterwards. It was Bell's first and only design to feature a tandem rotor layout, having a Pratt & Whitney R-2800-50 radial engine mounted at the rear and driving a transmission shaft to the

front pylon. Standard Bell 2-blade rotors were fitted fore and aft, with provision for folding them for stowage on board ship. The first XHSL-1 made its maiden flight on 4 March 1953.

Equipment on board the HSL-1 included electronic tracking gear and dunking sonar and its 4,000 lb (1,814 kg) cargo load could include bombs, depth charges or Fairchild AUM-N-2 Petrel air-to-underwater missiles. The crew was made up of 2 pilots and 2 sonar operators. Production orders were given for seventy-eight HSL-1's, of which eighteen were scheduled for delivery to the Fleet Air Arm under the Mutual Defense Assistance Program; but the Korean war had ended by the time the XHSL-1 test programme was completed, with the result that the British machines were not delivered and only fifty of those for the US Navy were completed. Delivery of these began in January 1957, to Squadron HU-1, but they spent most of their brief career on training duties. The HO4S, which the HSL-1 had been intended to replace, remained in service until the appearance of the HSS-1 anti-submarine version of the Sikorsky S-58.

83 **Vertol UH-25 and HUP Retriever**

This tandem-rotor design was evolved by Piasecki Helicopter Corporation to meet a Bureau of Aeronautics requirement, issued in 1945, for a utility helicopter to be based aboard aircraft carriers and other large warships of the US

Navy for search and rescue, plane guard and general transportation duties. The proposed aircraft was given the works designation PV-14 and two XHJP-1 prototypes (37976 and '77) were completed for US Navy evaluation. In 1948 work began on thirty-two PV-18's, or HUP-1 Retrievers, as the production version was known. They differed little from the original XHJP-1, the major apparent change being the addition of inward-sloping endplate fins to the horizontal stabilisers below the rear rotor head. Both sets of 3-blade rotors could be folded for shipboard stowage and the HUP-1, powered by a single 525 hp Continental R-975-34 piston engine, could accommodate 4–5 passengers or 3 casualty litters in addition to the 2-man crew.

Successful tests with a Sperry autopilot in the XHJP-1 enabled the next model, the HUP-2, to be built without tail surfaces and the more powerful Continental R-975-42 was installed in this and all subsequent production models. Another feature of the Retriever was a large rectangular rescue hatch offset to starboard in the floor of the front fuselage, through which a winch inside the cabin could lift weights of up to 400 lb (181 kg) at a time. One hundred and sixty-five HUP-2's were built for the US Navy; fifteen were supplied to France's Aéronavale, and the US Navy also operated about a dozen HUP-2S submarine-hunting aircraft with dunking sonar equipment. Another HUP-2 was given a sealed, watertight hull and outrigged twin floats for waterborne

tests. US Navy units, which included HU-1 and HU-2, began to receive the Retriever in February 1949.

In 1951 the US Air Force, on behalf of the Army, ordered a version of the HUP-2 with a reinforced cabin floor and hydraulically boosted controls, for general support and evacuation work. Seventy of these were delivered as H-25A Army Mules from 1953, as were fifty similar Naval HUP-3's (including three for the Royal Canadian Navy) for ambulance and light cargo duties. Production of the last aircraft was completed in July 1954. A proposal to boost the speed, range and payload of all H-25/HUP aircraft still in service by refitting them with 700 hp Wright R-1300-3 engines did not take place, and by the time the new tri-service designation system was introduced in July 1962 only the HUP-2 and HUP-3 remained in service; these became the UH-25B and UH-25C respectively.

84 Bristol 173 and Westland (Bristol) 192 Belvedere

The Belvedere general-purpose transport helicopter, which entered service with the RAF in the autumn of 1961, had its origins in the Bristol Type 173, two prototypes of which were begun in 1948 to Ministry of Supply Specification E.4/47. The first of these, the Type 173 Mk 1 G-ALBN, made its first flight on 3 January 1952. Bristol's first tandem-rotor helicopter design, it was powered by two 550 hp Alvis Leonides nine-cylinder engines and had a design gross weight of

10,600 lb (4,808 kg), with accommodation for 2 crew and 10 passengers. The Sycamore-type 3-blade rotor systems were interconnected for synchronisation and to enable either engine to maintain the drive in the event of an engine failure. In 1953, as XF785, it undertook sea trials on board HMS *Eagle*. The second prototype (Type 173 Mk 2) was essentially similar to the first, differing principally in landing gear and in the fitting of stub wings which served to off-load the rotors by some 30 per cent in forward flight. This aircraft (G-AMJI) flew for the first time on 31 August 1953. Later, with the stub wings removed to improve hover performance, and a dihedral tailplane, it also undertook sea trials (as XH379) before being loaned to BEA in August 1956 for trials. It was written off in 1957 after a landing accident.

Although reasonably successful aircraft for their day, the Type 173 prototypes had a poor engine-out performance, which was attributable to the non-availability of the Bristol Janus turbine engine originally intended for them. An attempt was made to overcome this situation, in the two Mk 3's that were built, by installing two 850 hp Alvis Leonides Major fourteen-cylinder piston-engines. The Mk 3's were otherwise similar to the Mk 2, and capable of accepting stub wings, but had a taller rear rotor pylon and operated at a gross weight of 13,500 lb (6,124 kg). However, cooling problems arose with these engines and, after protracted ground running in an effort to overcome this, only limited hover-

ing was achieved by the Mk 3 in late 1956. The Type 173's history was completed by one Mk 5, also intended for naval trials and for a Leonides Major powerplant. It had a shortened fuselage, to permit use on standard carrier lifts, and a long-stroke landing gear similar to that of the proposed Type 191 which by then was in an advanced state of design. Unfortunately, the engine problems encountered on the Mk 3's were of such magnitude that the Mk 5 never had its engines installed.

To meet the Royal Navy's requirement H.R. 146, and a similar contemporary Royal Canadian Navy specification (H.R. 149), Bristol submitted two tandem-rotor helicopter designs, the Types 191 and 193. These were basically similar to one another, the Type 191 being proposed in Series 1 (Leonides Major) and Series 2 (Napier Gazelle turbine) variants while the Canadian submission involved the use of Gazelles only. At the same time, to meet RAF requirement H.R. 150 for a general-purpose helicopter, the Type 192 was proposed, also with Series 1 and 2 options, and contracts were awarded in April 1956 for all three submissions. Orders were placed for three Type 191 Series 1, sixty-five Type 191 Series 2, twenty-two Type 192 Series 1 or 2, and four Type 193. A year later, however, the still-unresolved engine troubles, coupled with some (not unexpected) transmission problems on ground-running of the third and fourth Type 173's, led the 1957 Defence White Paper to cancel all orders for the Type 191. A Canadian economy drive similarly ended hope for the Type 193, which was to have been built in Canada.

The Type 192 order was, however, increased to twenty-six, including one prototype, and all effort was concentrated on the Gazelle-powered Type 192 Series 2. As the first three Type 191 fuselage shells had been completed, the first two were converted to accept Gazelle engines and were used for gantry testing of the Type 192 transmission. The third fuselage was fitted with Type 192 controls and commissioned as a control fatigue test rig. The Type 192 prototype (XG447) flew for the first time on 5 July 1958. In its initial configuration the aircraft had a manual control system, wooden rotor blades, small wheels, top-hinged main cabin doors and pilots' doors, and an anhedral tailplane with vertical endplate fins. Major external changes during the early flying were associated with correcting mild 'Dutch roll' characteristics. Various permutations of endplate fin attitude were assessed, culminating in a new long-chord anhedral tailplane without endplates, positioned further forward and lower than on the prototype. This tailplane was fitted to the second and fourth aircraft (XG448 and XG451), both of which began flying in 1959. The third type 192 (XG450) also flew for a limited period in 1959 with an electrically-actuated control trimming gear and a cartridge-actuated, liquid-fuelled engine starting system. By this time a rudimentary power assistance had been added to the cyclic control system on XG447/448/451; and XG450 was taken out of the flying programme to be fitted with a nose extensively modified to a fully-duplicated power-operated flying control standard. The fifth aircraft (XG452), flown in February 1960, was fitted with large wheels, oleo fairings, sliding cockpit doors and main cabin doors, metal rotor blades, power assistance on all control channels, and (for production reasons only) the final tailplane configuration, achieved by inverting the endplate fins originally used and inclining them to produce a 'double anhedral' effect.

An initial C of A release, for limited Service use, was given in mid-1960, and in the following October the seventh, eighth and tenth aircraft (XG453/4/6) were delivered to the trials unit at RAF Odiham. These pre-production aircraft approximated closely to XG451 in build state, with manual controls, small wheels and long-chord tailplane. On 12 December 1960, XG450, having had its major 'surgery' completed, flew with power-operated controls. This had necessitated a deepened front fuselage profile, a blister at the nose of the front fuselage fairing to cater for hydraulic pumps and tanks, and additional engine intake screening with deeper engine belly panels; remaining external improvements were as flown and proven on XG452, which had carried out the tropical trials programme in Tripoli in June 1960. This became the definitive standard for production aircraft, known as Belvederes; delivery of these began in August 1961 with XG457, the eleventh aircraft, following full C of A release in the previous March. Twenty-four aircraft were delivered to the RAF, which involved reworking all aircraft used for development and pre-production flying except XG450 (which remained on test flying) and the prototype, XG447.

The first unit to receive the Belvedere was No 66 Squadron, in September 1961, followed by Nos 26 and 72 Squadrons in 1962. As the Belvedere HC Mk 1 it served in the United Kingdom, Middle East and Far East. Carrying a 2-man crew, the Belvedere could lift 18-25 fully-equipped troops or 12 stretcher cases, according to the range required; its maximum range was 445 miles (716 km). Internal cargo load was 6,000 lb (2,722 kg); an external load of up to 5,250 lb (2,381 kg) could be lifted on an under-fuselage sling. The Belvedere was finally withdrawn from RAF service in March 1969, one aircraft (XG474) being allocated for display in the RAF Museum.

85 Yakovlev Yak-24 ('Horse')

It was not until late summer 1952 that the USSR made its first major effort to close the design gap between itself and the USA in regard to large transport helicopters. Two basic projects were selected, the first, for a 12-passenger aircraft of single main rotor configuration, being assigned to the Mil design bureau. The second, entrusted to the bureau headed by Aleksandir S. Yakovlev,

was for a twin-engined, tandem-rotor type capable of seating 24 passengers. Prototype flights of both types were required to take place within one year.

Two flying prototypes of the Yakovlev design were completed, the first making its maiden flight in the hands of S. Brovtsev and Y. Milyutichev on 3 July 1953; two others were built for static and dynamic testing. Two 1,700 hp Shvetsov ASh-82V radial engines drove rotor and transmission systems basically identical to those already proven in the single-engined Mi-4, with each engine geared to drive one or both rotors. Unfortunately this arrangement, although intended as a precaution against failure of either engine, created the problem of 'sympathetic' vibration. From the outset, vibration hampered the Yak-24's development, aggravated no doubt by insufficient rigidity in the fabric-covered rotor blades and middle section of the fuselage. After only 178 hours of operation, the rear engine frame attachments of the static test prototype collapsed and, in the words of the designer,* the rear rotor 'lunged forwards and the rotor blades began to chop the machine to pieces'. A satisfactory cure was eventually attained by cropping 50 cm (19·68 in) off each rotor blade, and state trials (during which another prototype was lost) began in late 1953. Production began about a year later, and the Yak-24 made its public debut in the Aviation Day display at Tushino in

*Notes of an Aircraft Designer, by A. S. Yakovlev.

July 1955, when four examples were exhibited. On 17 December 1955 a Yak-24 set two new world-class payload-to-altitude records. The early Yak-24's featured a Vee tailplane, but later production examples had rectangular endplate fins on a horizontal tailplane, and both versions were seen with and without a narrow central auxiliary rudder.

Initial Yak-24 production was undertaken on behalf of the Aviatsya-Vozdushnye Dessentnich Vosk (Aviation of the Airborne Troops), in which configuration the aircraft could accommodate up to 40 fully-equipped troops according to range. Other typical loads of the Letayuchy Vagon (Flying Wagon), as it was quickly dubbed, included 18 casualty litters, 2 anti-tank guns, 2 GAZ-69 command vehicles or 3 M-20 staff cars. In 1958 the Yak-24U became the standard military model, with all-metal rotor blades and fuselage skin, the revised tail configuration already mentioned, and the rotors restored to the original 21·00 m (68 ft 10¾ in) diameter. Civil counterpart to the Yak-24U was the Yak-24A, with standard seating for 30 passengers. The Yak-24A could also be operated as a freighter or flying crane, being able to lift an external sling load of 5,000 kg (11,023 lb). In 1960 the short-fuselage Yak-24K, a 9-seat executive version, was announced, and in the following year details were released of the 39-seat Yak-24P with 2,700 shp Ivchenko turboshaft engines. Neither of these is thought to have been built in quantity, and

overall production of the earlier variants was probably not high.

86 Mil Mi-12 ('Homer')

Western observers received their first sight of this massive helicopter at the 1971 Paris Air Show, although its existence had then been known for more than 2 years. Its design was started in 1965, to meet an original requirement for a tandem-rotor helicopter capable of lifting vertically ballistic missiles and other large loads comparable with those of the giant Antonov An-22 conventional transport aircraft. The Mil design bureau, however, believed that better results could be achieved by adopting the present configuration of a winged helicopter with the powerplant in wingtip nacelles driving side-by-side rotors. The capabilities of the Mi-12 (known alternatively as the V-12) were strikingly demonstrated on 22 February 1969, when it lifted a 68,410 lb (31,030 kg) payload to a height of 9,682 ft (2,951 m), climbing at a rate of more than 600 ft (180 m) per minute. Six months later, on 6 August 1969, an Mi-12 with a 6-man crew lifted an 88,636 lb (40,204·5 kg) payload to a height of 7,398 ft (2,255 m). As a measure of this performance, the payload alone on this occasion was more than double the *gross take-off weight* of the largest helicopter in the western world.

It was reported that the original Mi-12 prototype crashed in 1969, but two others were flying by the summer of 1971. The freight compartment of the fuselage, access to which is gained via two upward-hinged clamshell doors and a downward-hinged ramp at the rear, is 92 ft 4 in (28·15 m) long and 14 ft 5 in (4·40 m) square. There are internal roof rails for an electrically-operated loading crane, and about 50 folding seats along the fuselage sides for troops or handling crews accompanying major loads. The 6-man flight crew consists of a pilot, co-pilot, flight engineer and electrician in the nose, and a navigator and radio operator in the upper cockpit. It was reported that production of the Mi-12 was to have begun in late 1971 or early 1972, probably incorporating some modifications including increased wing camber instead of trailing-edge flaps. Although developed primarily for the Soviet armed forces, the Mi-12 will probably be employed also by Aeroflot for such tasks as the transport of heavy machinery and the support of oil or natural gas drilling operations.

87 & 88 **Vertol Model 43, CH-21 Work Horse and Shawnee, and Vertol Model 44**

This long-serving helicopter was a development of the original Piasecki PV-3 and a direct descendant of the PV-17 or HRP-2 Rescuer first flown in late 1949. A 10-seater, the HRP-2 was a radical redesign of the HRP-1, powered by a 600 hp R-1340 piston engine. Only five were built, being used by the US Marine Corps for assault troop training, but from this aircraft was developed the Piasecki PD-22, which, as the XH-21, flew for the first time on 11 April 1952. Eighteen

YH-21's were ordered for service trials with the US Air Force, and in September 1953 one of these aircraft established new FAI helicopter speed and altitude records in its class of 146·735 mph (236·147 km/hr) and 22,289 ft (6,794 m). Only a few weeks later the first YH-21 was delivered to the USAF. Service tests included practical operational experience, for several of the trials batch were assigned to Arctic search and rescue duty where they carried out a great deal of useful work in temperatures down to − 54°C.

First USAF production version, the H-21A Work Horse, was basically similar to the YH-21, having a 1,425 hp Wright R-1820-103 engine derated to 1,150 hp and a gross weight of 11,500 lb (5,217 kg). Accommodation provided for a 2-man crew and 12 casualty litters or 14 seated passengers. Thirty-two H-21A's were built for the USAF and these also were employed primarily for Arctic search and rescue duties. They were followed by one hundred and sixty-three H-21B assault transports, seating up to 20 troops. The H-21B utilised the full 1,425 hp available from the R-1820-103 engine and was fitted with an autopilot. Among the duties carried out by H-21B's were supplying and supporting the off-shore 'Texas Tower' stations in the North American DEW-Line radar chain. Others were used by the MATS in the rescue role as HH-21B's (previously SH-21B's). The standard H-21A and B became CH-21A and B in 1962.

When Piasecki Helicopter Corporation became Vertol Aircraft Corporation in 1956 the H-21A and H-21B were given the new Model number 42. The Vertol Model 43, first flown that spring, was basically identical to the H-21B and was produced in large numbers as the H-21C Shawnee tactical and logistics transport for the US Army. It was redesignated CH-21C in July 1962. The Shawnee bore most of the brunt of Army support during the early stages of the US campaign in Vietnam, and three hundred and thirty-four H-21C's were eventually built for the US Army and for export. The major foreign recipient was France, to whose Aviation Légère de l'Armée de Terre ninety-eight were supplied; ten were delivered to the Aéronavale. The original twenty-six ordered by the Federal German Heeresfliegerei were later more than doubled. Five H-21B's were delivered to Canada, supplementing an earlier batch of six H-21A's and being operated by Spartan Air Service on behalf of the RCAF in support of the Mid-Canada Radar Line. The Japan Air Self Defence Force also received six H-21B's.

Late in 1957 two experimental variants of the H-21 were flown. These were the Vertol 71 (H-21D) and Vertol 105, powered respectively by two General Electric T58 and two Lycoming T53 turboshaft engines, but development of these was abandoned in favour of the Boeing-Vertol 107 (which see). One H-21C was tested experimentally

with a machine-gun mounted in the cabin doorway and brackets on the main undercarriage members to carry up to four more guns or rocket pods. Several other H-21C's have been employed for flying crane duties.

First flown in the spring of 1956, the Vertol 44 originated as the Piasecki PH-42, and was essentially a refined version of the military H-21, produced for the commercial market and for export. Powerplant was the civil version of the H-21's Wright R-1820-103 radial engine, and alterations to the Model 44 included all-metal rotor blades and automatic stabilisation equipment to improve the aircraft's handling qualities. Drag-reducing refinement of the fuselage enabled the Vertol 44 to operate at a higher gross weight than its predecessor.

The Vertol 44 was granted type approval by the FAA in April 1957 and was offered in three basic versions. The Model 44A was a civil or military utility model accommodating 19 passengers, 20 troops, 12 stretchers or 2,500 lb (1,134 kg) of cargo. The Model 44B, distinguishable by its oval cabin windows, was a 15-seat airline version; while the Model 44C was offered as an executive helicopter with custom-designed interior layout.

Success of the Vertol 44 was limited, owing to the imminence of the turbine-powered Model 107. Military models were sold to Sweden, whose Navy received nine Model 44A's for employment on anti-submarine duties with the designation HKP 1; two other

44A's were delivered to the Japan Ground Self Defence Force, and three to Canada to supplement RCAF H-21's operated by Spartan. The only airline to employ the 44B regularly was New York Airways, which had five, though two were leased to Sabena in 1958. Two 44B's were purchased by the French government, and a fact not widely known is that one 44B and one 44C were acquired by the Soviet government. Other sales were made to private companies, in the construction and oil industries among others. The Swedish Model 44's – and those used by New York Airways – were given watertight lower fuselages and provided with inflatable flotation bags above each leg of the tricycle landing gear, to enable them to land on or take off from water in an emergency.

89 & 90 **Boeing-Vertol Model 107**

Soon after the former Piasecki Helicopter Corporation changed its title to Vertol Aircraft Corporation in March 1956, a design study programme was initiated to evolve a medium transport helicopter, with civil and military applications, to be powered by a pair of the lightweight, economical gas turbine engines then becoming available. The project was given the works Model number 107 and construction of a prototype (N74060) was put in hand in May 1957. Later that year flight tests were conducted with two H-21 helicopters in which a twin-turbine powerplant had been installed, and on 22 April 1958 the prototype Vertol 107 made its maiden flight. Powered by two 860 shp Lycoming T53 turboshaft engines, it was designed to seat 25 passengers with a stewardess and a flight crew of 2. However, the first interest came from the US Army, which in July 1958 ordered ten modified aircraft as YHC-1A's. The first of these (58-5514) was flown on 27 August 1959. With the ordering of the YHC-1B Chinook test batch two months before this, the YHC-1A order was cut back to three aircraft, and the third YHC-1A, with 1,050 shp General Electric T58-GE-6 engines and rotors of increased diameter, was later converted to a commercial configuration as the Vertol 107-II-1. It flew in its new form on 25 October 1960, by which time Vertol had become a division of The Boeing Company.

This was followed on 19 May 1961 by the first flight of N6671, a company-sponsored production prototype, with square cabin windows and taller rotor pylons and 1,250 shp CT58-110-1 engines, tailored to the requirements of New York Airways. This airline subsequently ordered five of these aircraft under the production designation 107-II-10 and, following FAA certification of the commercial passenger version in January 1962, opened regular services with its 107's on 1 July. Three more were purchased by Pan American and leased to NYA.

A modified version of the YHC-1A, the Boeing-Vertol 107M, was in February 1961 declared winner of a design competition held to find a medium assault transport helicopter for the US Marine Corps, and this aircraft was ordered into production as the HRB-1 (CH-46A from July 1962) with the name Sea Knight. The modest initial batch of fourteen was subsequently increased until by the end of 1970 six hundred Sea Knights had been ordered. This total includes CH-46D's, with 1,400 shp T58-GE-10 engines and slightly bigger diameter rotors with cambered blades; and CH-46F's, which are similar but carry additional electronic equipment. The CH-46 models carry a flight crew of 3 and up to 25 troops (or 15 casualty litters and 2 medical attendants), have a rear loading ramp and power-folding for the rotor blades. They serve, or have served, as assault or logistics transports with Marine Corps squadrons in the Atlantic, Pacific and Mediterranean as well as in Vietnam. The US Navy has corresponding models designated UH-46A (twenty-four built) and UH-46D based aboard its Fast Combat Support Ships for the 'vertical replenishment' of supplies to combat vessels at sea.

Exported Vertol-built military 107's includes six 107-II-9's supplied to the RCAF as CH-113 Labrador search and rescue aircraft and ten 107-II-14's to the Swedish Air Force for similar duties; the Canadian Army had twelve CH-113A Voyageur cargo transports and the Royal Swedish Navy four 107-II-15's with sonar gear and a towing hook for submarine search and minesweeping duties. Both Swedish versions (which are designated HKP 4) are powered

by Rolls-Royce Bristol Gnome H.1200 turbine engines.

The exclusive right to build and market all civil models, and military versions other than those for the US and Canada, was in 1965 vested with the Kawasaki Aircraft Co. This company was in 1972 the sole manufacturer of this aircraft, production by Boeing having ended. The Japanese-built version, known as the KV-107/II, was certificated by the FAA in November 1965 and in 1972 was offered in seven different versions. Kawasaki had by then completed ten KV-107/II-2 25-seat airline models including three for Thailand, two for Pan American (the latter being operated by NYA), one for New York Airways, and two for Air Lift Inc of Japan (formerly Kanki Airlines). Military orders include sixteen KV-107/II-3 for the JMSDF (for mine countermeasures), seventy-six KV-107/II-4 for the JGSDF (tactical cargo/troop transport), thirty KV-107/11-5 for the JASDF (search and rescue), and seven Gnome-powered -5's (as HKP 7's) for the Swedish Navy. No examples have yet been completed of the utility KV-107/II-1 or de luxe -6, but one -7 VIP transport was sold to Thailand in 1964. Kawasaki has also flown, on 3 April 1968, a prototype KV-107/IIA, an improved-performance version with 1,400 shp CT58-140-1 engines.

91 Boeing-Vertol CH-47 Chinook

In March 1959, from five entrants, the US Army declared the Vertol 114 winner of its design competition for a 'battlefield mobility' helicopter, and three months later placed an order for five YHC-1B prototypes for service tests. While waiting for these to materialise it purchased three YHC-1A's, which were basically militarised versions of the civil Model 107 and subsequently followed a separate line of development into the CH-46 Sea Knight.

The YHC-1B was altogether a much larger machine, as was necessary to meet the US Army's requirement that it should be able to carry loads of 2 tons internally or 8 tons externally. The first flight of a YHC-1B was made on 21 September 1961 and the first delivery to the US Army in August 1962. In the new tri-service designation system introduced in mid-1962 the prototypes were restyled YCH-47A; they, and the initial small production batch of five CH-47A's, were powered by 2,200 shp Lycoming T55-L-5 turboshafts, but all subsequent CH-47A's have the 2,650 shp L-7 version of this engine. The first orders for the CH-47A were of modest size, but such has been the increase in the requirement for these aircraft that by the beginning of 1972 six hundred and eighty-one Chinooks of all versions had been delivered, of which more than four hundred had been employed in Vietnam. The CH-47 replaced various earlier types and is now the US Army's standard medium transport helicopter, used as an assault transport, aircraft recovery or casualty evacuation vehicle. In 1972 it began also to equip units of the US Army National Guard and Army Reserve. The capacious watertight fuselage will accommodate from 33 to 44 armed troops, 24 casualty litters with 2 attendants, major components of the Pershing missile system, or a capacity payload (CH-47A) of 6,150 lb (2,790 kg) over a mission radius of 115 miles (185 km). In June 1965 the US Army ordered four aircraft to be completed as ACH-47A's; the first of these was flown five months later, and in 1966 three were operating under combat conditions in Vietnam, but this version was not ordered in quantity.

In early October 1966 the first of two prototype YCH-47B's was flown, this version differing from the A model in having 2,850 shp T55-L-7C engines, an 8,850 lb (4,014 kg) short-range payload and rotor blades of slightly greater diameter with cambered leading edges. Delivery of CH-47B's to the US Army began in May 1967. First deliveries commenced in spring 1968 of the CH-47C, a further development flown for the first time on 14 October 1967. This has 3,750 shp T55-L-11 engines and gross weight increased to 46,000 lb (20,865 kg). A co-production and marketing agreement for the CH-47C was reached in spring 1968 between Boeing and Meridionali of Italy. Beginning with five CH-47C's supplied by Boeing in 1971, Meridionali is to complete, initially, eighteen Chinooks for the Imperial Iranian Air Force and Army and twenty-six for the Italian Army. The Vietnamese Air Force has received about fifty CH-47A's since 1971, and in

1972 twelve CH-47C's were ordered by the Royal Australian Air Force and six by the Spanish Army.

Boeing is currently developing, as a potential successor to the Chinook, the tilt-wing Model 347 which flew for the first time (without the wings fitted) on 27 May 1970. This aircraft has a stretched Chinook fuselage, 4-blade larger-diameter rotors and retractable landing gear.

92 Westland (Fairey) Rotodyne

In the House of Commons on 16 July 1959 the then Minister of Transport and Civil Aviation said of the Rotodyne: 'The view of BEA and my view is that it is a winner'; yet less than three years later this highly advanced aeroplane was abandoned because these same two authorities lacked the faith to give it continued support. This was a bad enough decision even then; less than six years later, the current British government's 'saving' of £10 million, by cancelling the Chinooks it had ordered only weeks before, revealed it to have been even more foolhardy. The same amount of money, spent on completing the Rotodyne's development in 1962, could have provided the RAF much sooner with a vehicle having far better carrying power, performance and operating costs than the Chinook.

The Rotodyne story began with a much smaller aeroplane, the Fairey Gyrodyne prototype G-AIKF, which first flew on 7 December 1947. This had a 525 hp Leonides piston engine driving a 51 ft 7½ in (15·74 m) 3-blade main rotor and a small tractor propeller in a fairing at the tip of its starboard stub wing. After setting a helicopter speed record of 124·3 mph (200 km/hr) in June 1948, the first Gyrodyne was destroyed in an accident during the following April; but a second similar machine (G-AJJP) was completed, and in 1954 this was converted into the Jet Gyrodyne XJ389 to test design features of the Rotodyne. The original 3-blade rotor was replaced by a 2-blade assembly and the shaft drive to the rotor was eliminated. Instead, Fairey-designed pressure jets were mounted at each blade tip, in which compressed air fed from the engine was ignited with kerosene to drive the rotor. Small pusher propellers were mounted at each of the wing-tips.

The Rotodyne prototype (XE521) was ordered by the Ministry of Supply in August 1953 and made its first vertical take-off on 6 November 1957. Early trials were carried out with the aircraft functioning purely as a helicopter, the first transition from a vertical take-off to forward flight being made on 10 April 1958. For this manoeuvre the entire power of the two Eland turboprop engines was transferred from the 4-blade rotor to the tractor propellers. On 5 January 1959 the Rotodyne set a closed circuit speed record of 191 mph (307·22 km/hr), exceeding the previous record by 49 mph (78·86 km/hr) and the existing absolute record for helicopters by 29 mph (46·67 km/hr). Later that year the wings were given ailerons and increased incidence, and the vertical tail surfaces were also revised. On 7 February 1960, XE521 resumed trials with an added central fin, shortened exhausts and a fully-faired rotor pylon.

The prototype had been built as a 40-seat aircraft with a crew of 3. When Westland acquired Fairey Aviation in 1960 it abandoned its own large helicopter, the Westminster, in favour of the Rotodyne, and with the help of £4 million government backing continued to develop an enlarged version to production standard. This became known as the Rotodyne Z (the prototype being restyled Rotodyne Y), and as envisaged at the time of its cancellation would have accommodated 57–75 passengers or 18,000 lb (8,165 kg) of freight in a 69 ft 5 in (21·16 m) fuselage and cruised at 230 mph (370 km/hr) on the power of two 5,250 ehp Rolls-Royce Tyne engines. Okanagan, the Canadian operator, had tentatively ordered one Rotodyne in 1958, and Indies Air of Puerto Rico signified its interest in the type in 1961. But the major potential customers were BEA and New York Airways, which declared their intent to order six and five respectively, each with an option to increase its fleet later to twenty. The Rotodyne Z had been designed with an eye also on military orders, with a fuselage cross-section capable of admitting standard British Army vehicles – a feature which, incidentally, would have made it equally useful as a commercial car ferry. Late in 1960 Westland was invited

to quote for building six Rotodynes for BEA and twelve troop/vehicle transports for the RAF; but when both airline and government declined either to order the aircraft or to contribute further towards its development Westland finally abandoned the project in February 1962 and the Rotodyne Z was never completed. Although lack of faith in the aircraft was the main cause of its demise, a contributory factor was the disproportionate publicity given to the noise made by the Rotodyne's tip-jets, which it was said would inhibit its use in city centres. In fact, well before the aircraft was abandoned this noise had been successfully decreased to less than that made by a London Underground train, which millions of people accept every day; and it had been estimated that this could have been reduced even further, to a level of 95 EPNdB – more than 10 decibels lower than the standard considered acceptable for large jet airliners at the beginning of the 1970s.

93 Kamov Ka-22 Vintokryl ('Hoop')

This large rotorcraft is the only known Soviet example of an attempt to produce an aeroplane to operate on similar principles to Britain's Rotodyne. It was seen by western observers only once, when a single example appeared in the Aviation Day display at Moscow in July 1961, in military insignia. The Vintokryl (the name means 'screw-wing') was evidently intended only as a research aircraft, and did not go into series production, but a statement by

Nikolai Kamov early in 1966 averred that the configuration was then 'still active'.

The Ka-22, like the Rotodyne, used conventional fixed wings to off-load the rotor system, but in the case of the Soviet machine the two engines were mounted in pods at the extremities of these wings, each driving a 4-blade main rotor immediately above it. A conventional single tail assembly was fitted, and the box-like fuselage included a rear loading ramp for large items of freight or military equipment. The Ka-22 appeared capable of transporting 80 or more soldiers and their equipment. Some indications of its capabilities were given in October and November 1961, when the aircraft established two FAI records for speed and six height-with-payload records. The records for speed in a straight line (221·4 mph = 356·3 km/hr) and for flight to a height of 8,491 ft (2,588 m) remained unbeaten by the autumn of 1972.

94 Piasecki 16H Pathfinder

The Piasecki Aircraft Corporation has been engaged since the early 1960s on a series of compound helicopter research designs known by the name Pathfinder. The concept first took material form as the Model 16H-1 Pathfinder prototype (registration N616H). This aircraft was developed as a private venture and flew for the first time on 21 February 1962, undertaking this flight as a 'pure' helicopter without using the 3-blade ducted tail fan. No wings were fitted at that stage, the cabin was unfaired, and the retractable landing gear was fixed in the extended position. Small stub-wings, which could be folded, and a fully-enclosed cabin to accommodate a pilot and 4 passengers, were added later in the year. Powered by a 550 shp UACL PT6B-2 turboshaft engine, the Pathfinder had a 41 ft 0 in (12·50 m) diameter 3-blade rotor, a fuselage length of 25 ft 0 in (7·62 m) and a gross weight of 5,700 lb (2,585 kg). In all, it amassed a total of 185 flying hours, during which speeds of up to 170 mph (273 km/hr) were attained. Subsequently, Piasecki received a joint US Army/US Navy contract to develop a compound helicopter capable of providing data on flight by such aircraft at speeds of up to 230 mph (370 km/hr). As part of this programme the original aircraft was redesigned to become the Model 16H-1A Pathfinder II, in which form it made its second 'first' flight on 15 November 1965. Modification work had begun in 1964, ground tests were carried out in the summer of 1965, and initial hovering trials were completed by the end of the year.

The principal design changes in the Pathfinder II were the enlargement of the fuselage, lengthened to accommodate 8 persons; the installation of a 1,250 shp General Electric T58-GE-5 engine; and the adoption of a larger-diameter rotor, a new drive system and a new tail fan. By May 1966 the Pathfinder II had flown some 40 hours, during which it had achieved level speeds of up to 225 mph (362 km/hr), had flown sideways at up to 35 mph (55 km/hr) and backwards at 32 mph (52 km/hr), and had made 20 auto-rotative flights. For the final phase of the Army/Navy programme, in the summer of 1966, it was refitted with a 1,500 shp T58-GE-5 engine, having new-design air intakes ahead of the wing leading edges, and received the new Model designation 16H-1C.

Since then Piasecki has announced several designs based upon the Pathfinder configuration, although up to 1972 none of these had been built. In 1968 it announced the Model 16H-3F Pathfinder III, a twin-turbine design using the 16H-1A fuselage with two T58-GE-10's and 4-blade rotor and tail fan, for search and rescue, ASW and military utility applications. The 16H-3H Heli-Plane project, for an 8-passenger executive transport with twin PT6 or TPE 331 engines, was superseded in 1969 by the 9/15-seat 16H-3J commercial transport project; this in turn was redesignated 16H-3K in 1971, following the proposal to install more powerful PT6B engines. In 1972 Piasecki was reported to be working on a high-performance development of the original Pathfinder, designated 16H-1HT, to seat a pilot and 4 passengers. Intended to be powered by a 986 shp Turboméca Astazou XVI engine, it was planned to have a maximum speed of 202 mph (325 km/hr) and a range of 440 miles (708 km).

Anti-torque rotor. Device to balance the torque effect created by the rotation of a powered main rotor. Normally takes the form of a small auxiliary rotor, mounted on the tail arm of a helicopter and driven by an extension shaft from the power source, which exerts a sideways thrust to push or pull against the torque effect. See also *Torque*.

Articulated rotor (Fig. 1). A rotor system in which, between the blades and the rotor head, there are flapping hinges, drag hinges and pitch change bearings about which each blade can move freely.

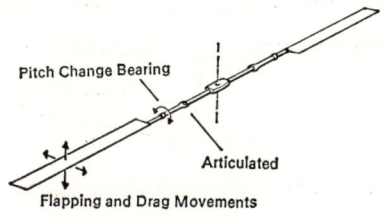

1. Articulated rotor.

Autogiro (Fig. 2). The name registered by Juan de la Cierva for his series of rotorcraft. Should always be used, in this spelling and with a capital 'A', in reference to gyroplanes of the Cierva type. See also *Autogyro*.

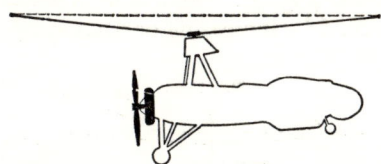

2. Autogiro : only forward propeller thrust is powered.

Autogyro. A rotorcraft which derives substantially all of its lift, throughout or during part of its flight, from an autorotating rotor system not provided with any form of direct power drive. This form of spelling, or the term Gyroplane, is used to distinguish craft of this type other than Autogiros (*q.v.*) of the

Cierva type. Unless fitted with jump-starting (*q.v.*), autogyros require a short take-off run to become airborne.

Autorotation. The ability of a rotor to 'windmill' solely by the action of the airflow on the blades, i.e. without any form of direct power drive. In a helicopter, the blades may be in auto-rotation when the power and the blade pitch angle are reduced (i.e. when descending); in an autogyro, they are autorotating throughout a flight.

Co-axial rotor system (Fig. 3). One in which the two main rotors have a common axis, one shaft turning inside the other. Co-axial systems are also contra-rotating (*q.v.*), each rotor cancelling

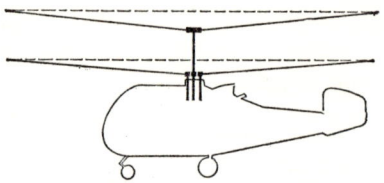

3. Co-axial contra-rotating rotor system.

out the torque effect of the other in forward flight. To change the direction of flight, a torque effect is induced deliberately by differential collective-pitch change between one rotor and the other.

Collective pitch control (Fig. 4). The means of causing a helicopter to ascend or descend by increasing or decreasing simultaneously

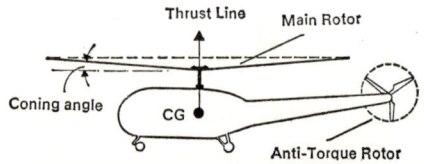

4. Collective pitch control (in the hover).

(i.e. collectively), by the same amount and in the same direction, the pitch angle of all blades of the main rotor(s).

Compound helicopter (Fig. 5). A helicopter, with the rotor(s) turning in a substantially horizontal plane at all times during flight, which also embodies a separate means of propulsion. A com-

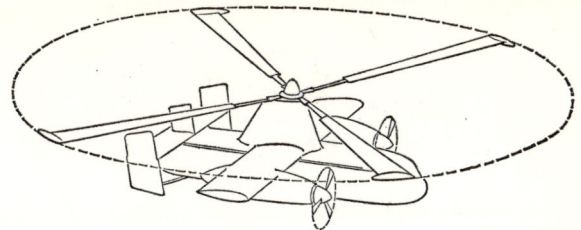

5. Compound helicopter.

pound helicopter need not have fixed wings, but those which do are able to fly with the lift requirement transferred substantially to the wings. With the forward-thrust requirement also transferred to the propulsion unit(s), the rotor(s) may then be in a substantially unloaded condition, but may still supply some or all of the control forces.

Coning angle (Figs. 4 and 7). Main rotor blades fitted with flapping hinges are free to rise to equalise the load imposed on the rotor disc, thereby describing the shape of a shallow cone. The angle between the undersides of the blades and a line perpendicular to the rotor thrust line is known as the coning angle.

Contra-rotating rotors. Main rotors (usually two) which rotate in opposite directions. They may be of the co-axial *(Fig. 3)*, intermeshing *(Fig. 12)*, outrigged side-by-side *(Fig. 6)* or tandem *(Fig. 16)* configuration.

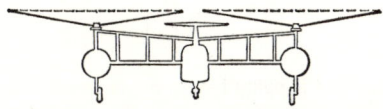

6. Contra-rotating (outrigged) rotor.

Convertible helicopter. A helicopter, capable by means of a mechanical conversion of flying purely as a fixed-wing aircraft, with the rotor(s) no longer serving a useful function, except possibly to produce some lift while in a stopped or autorotating condition (i.e., serving the function of fixed wings). Included in this category are such types as the stopped/lifting rotor, stopped/stowed rotor and tilt-rotor aircraft.

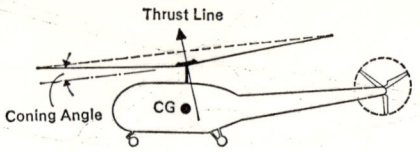

7. Cyclic pitch control (in sustained forward flight).

Cyclic pitch control (Fig. 7). The means of causing a helicopter to change its direction of level flight by changing the pitch angle of each main rotor blade consecutively (i.e. cyclically) according to its geometric position during each revolution, so tilting the theoretical axis of rotation in the direction of flight required. To tilt the rotor disc forward when translating from hovering to forward flight, the pitch angle is decreased on each blade as it advances and increased as it retreats.

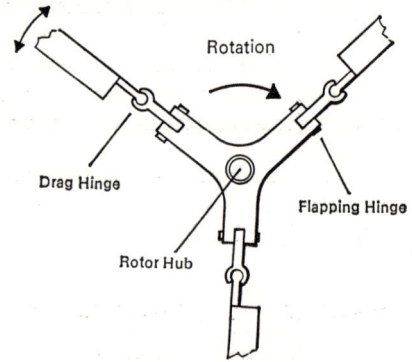

8. Drag and flapping hinges on an articulated rotor.

Drag hinge (Fig. 8); also known as *Lag hinge*. A hinge in the vertical plane, adjacent to the root of each main rotor blade, permitting the blade to move freely backwards or forwards in a horizontal plane in relation to the other blades or to the rotor hub, and so eliminate bending moment.

Flapping hinge (Fig. 9). A hinge in the horizontal plane, adjacent to the root of each main rotor blade, permitting each blade to flap (i.e. to rise and fall) independently of the other blade(s) as it rotates.

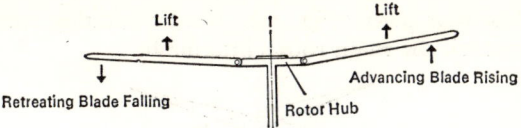

9. Principle of the flapping hinge.

Ground effect (Fig. 10): also known as *Ground cushion*. Supplementary source of lift, available when a helicopter is hovering near to the ground with the rotor disc substantially level. It is caused by the down-wash of air from the rotor being reflected back upwards from the ground to form a cushion of air beneath the rotor disc.

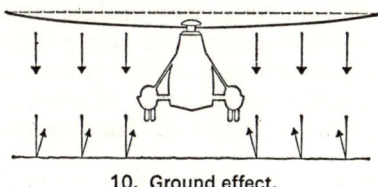

10. Ground effect.

Ground resonance. Phenomenon which can occur on the ground if a rotor system is unbalanced, i.e. if the rotor's actual centre of gravity has become displaced from its geometric centre (see page 9).

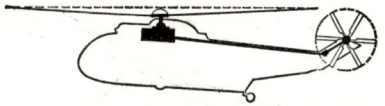

11. Helicopter (main and tail rotors both powered).

Helicopter (Fig. 11). A rotorcraft, capable of sustained hovering, which derives substantially all of its lift, throughout its flight, from a power-driven rotor system with a fixed and substantially vertical shaft. In a 'pure' helicopter the rotor(s) turn in a substantially horizontal plane and, throughout the flight, supply the aerodynamic forces for propulsion and most of the aerodynamic forces for lift. Most winged helicopters also fall within this category, in that the wings supply only a small proportion of the total lift. See also *Compound helicopter* and *Convertible helicopter*.

Intermeshing rotor system (Fig. 12). Contra-rotating rotor system (*q.v.*) in which the main rotors intermesh.

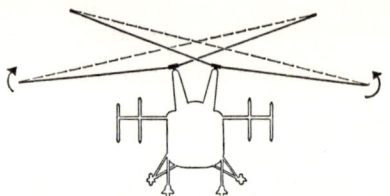

12. Intermeshing contra-rotating twin rotors.

Jump-starting. System enabling an autogyro to become airborne without a take-off run. Power is applied for initial spin-up of the rotor, and by mounting the drag hinges obliquely the rotor blades can swing forward to a positive pitch angle, after power has been disengaged from the rotor, to provide enough lift for the aircraft to jump into the air and translate to forward flight.

Pitch change. Increasing or decreasing the angle of pitch of a rotor blade.

Rigid rotor (Fig. 13). An integral unit without blade flexibility or articulation, i.e. free to change pitch or to 'see-saw' on the rotor shaft, but not fitted with flapping or drag hinges.

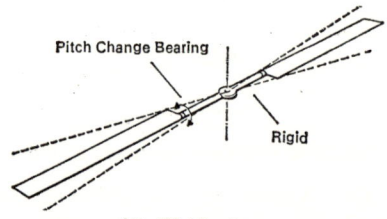

13. Rigid rotor.

Rotor head. See Fig. 14. The collective pitch control (H) raises or lowers the swashplate (J), increasing or decreasing pitch on all blades simultaneously. The cyclic pitch control (G) tilts the swashplate via the spherical bearing (C) in the desired direction of flight, making an angle to the rotor hub. This puts on or takes off pitch on each individual blade at a varying rate according to its position relative to the tilt, producing the effect of inclining the theoretical axis of the rotor disc in the required direction of flight.

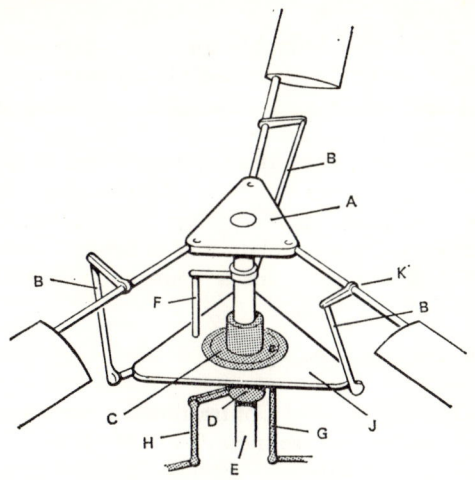

14. Rotor head assembly.

A Drag and flapping hinge assembly.
B Pitch change arm.
C Spherical bearing.
D Sliding sleeve.
E Rotor shaft.

F Scissor link driving swashplate.
G Cyclic pitch control.
H Collective pitch control.
J Swashplate.
K Pitch change bearing.

Rotorcraft. Generic term for all aircraft which derive, for all or part of their flight, the whole or a substantial part of their lift from a rotor system, comprising a set of external blades arranged to rotate about a substantially vertical axis.

Semi-rigid rotor (Fig. 15). An integral unit, without blade articulation (i.e. with no individual flapping or drag hinges), but which has limited flexibility in the flapping and dragging planes is and also free to 'see-saw' or 'teeter' about a central gimbal.

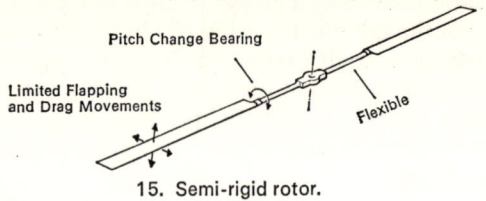

15. Semi-rigid rotor.

Swashplate. A two-part assembly for conveying a cyclic-pitch change to the rotor blades. It consists of an inner and an outer section, the latter driven by a scissor link from the rotor shaft, rotating with the rotor, and capable of being tilted in any direction; the inner, non-rotating section is free only to tilt. A spherical bearing attaches the swashplate to the fixed casing of the rotor head, and pitch-change arms attached to the rotating section of the swashplate link the rotor blades directly to the cyclic control run, via a connection from the non-rotating section.

Tail rotor. See *Anti-torque rotor.*

Tandem rotor system (Fig. 16). Contra-rotating rotor system (*q.v.*) in which the main rotors are mounted in tandem.

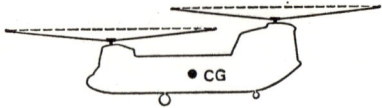

16. Tandem rotor configuration.

Torque. Reaction of the fuselage of a rotorcraft to the turning of the main rotor, by tending to rotate in the opposite direction. In a single-main-rotor helicopter, this effect is counteracted by a separate anti-torque rotor (*q.v.*); in helicopters with contra-rotating rotor systems (*q.v.*), each rotor cancels out the torque effect of the other, except when an application of differential torque is required in order to change the direction of flight.

Winged helicopter. See *Helicopter* and *Compound helicopter.*

INDEX

The reference numbers refer to the
illustrations and corresponding text.